D1577228

CLASHMACLAVERS

CLASHMACLAVERS

A MIXTY-MAXTY
OF PROSE AND VERSE
IN THE COUTHY TRADITION

BY

LAVINIA DERWENT

OLIVER & BOYD
EDINBURGH : TWEEDDALE COURT
LONDON : 98 GREAT RUSSELL STREET, W.C.

2081914 21

√ 91,226

First Edition . . 1947

RESERVE

THIS BOOK IS SET IN 11 POINT GARAMOND

PRINTED IN GREAT BRITAIN FOR THE PUBLISHERS
BY ROBERT CUNNINGHAM AND SONS LTD. ALVA

PREFACE

This book is designed for those who are neither afraid to read or speak the doric, nor think it " common " to use familiarly such expressive words as scunner, slaister and stravaig. To a true Scot there are some thoughts which can be expressed only in his own native language. Translated into English the subtle shading of meaning, which can only be captured by the sturdy doric, is diverted and something is lost in the translation.

An old sweetie-wife once said : " I whiles have to speak to ma mair perjinct customers in the English, but dodsakes ! yon's no' a language to do your *thinkin'* in. I wad as sune try the Greek. An' as for havin' a guid-gaun blether, gie me the doric every time. I'm blessed if I could gie onybody their character in cauld English."

And so with thanks to the old sweetie-wives and others who have unconsciously posed for these pen-portraits, I hope that this book may divert those who still care for clashmaclavers in the old couthy tongue.

ACKNOWLEDGMENTS

For permission to include Poems and Sketches, I would like to thank the Editors of the following papers:

EDINBURGH EVENING DISPATCH
The Kirk Moose, The Dambrod, "Jerry" Didn't Come, The Baneshaker, Pebble Kail.

GLASGOW EVENING TIMES
The Moose, On Leave, Caged, The Ragman, Nature's Lesson, City Speug, The Sodger's Lament, Hame Thochts, Saturday Penny, The Auld Angler, It's a Quiet Life in the City, Mrs. McWhirter on the "Tellyphone," Man on the Wireless, Solemn Occasion, Little Old Lady, The Dockside Smiddy "The Wee Doctor," Charlie the Cheapjack, Uncle Andra's Car, Village Blitzkrieg, Pavement Artist.

S.M.T. MAGAZINE
Big Bella the Bondager, The Village Bobby, The Village Fair, Kate the Cadger, The Travelling Geggie.

GLASGOW EVENING NEWS
The Kirk Pillar, The Elder, The Gloamin'.

PEOPLE'S FRIEND
Hame on Leave, The Worshipper.

GLASGOW HERALD
Design for Living.

WEEKLY SCOTSMAN

A Nicht at the Kirn.

CHAMBERS'S JOURNAL

Kist o' Whustles, The Betheral, The Unctioneer, The Dambrod, The Mendin', The Bondager, The Bobby, The Doctor, The Village Bus, The Spaewife, The Kirk Choir, The Plunker, The Roup, The Precentor.

PEOPLE'S JOURNAL

" Inside " Information, Bella the Postie.

EDINBURGH EVENING NEWS

The Country Train, Queue, The Auld Herd, The Porter, Hero, The Meenister, The Auld Dominie, The Ben-End, Thoughts in Church, The Auld Stane, Pavement Artist, The Gypsy Queen, The Drove Road, Fame, Sabbath Schule, The Dyker.

*   *   *

For rights to read any of these poems or sketches in public, application should be made to Cecil Hunt, 11 Poultry, Cheapside, London, E.C. 2.

CONTENTS

PROSE

VERSE

CONTENTS

THE KIRK MOOSE

There has always been a kirk moose in our Church. It is as kenspeckle a sight as Mrs. Macnab's Sabbath bonnet, or the wart on the beadle's nose, and a great deal more entertaining than either.

Perhaps it is not always the same moose—if so, it must have long since passed its allotted span—but, at least, it looks the same, and has the same habit of sitting solemnly on its hunkers, and polishing its whiskers to the tune of *French*.

Its stronghold is a hole somewhere in the region of the pulpit stairs, but during the service it is distinctly mobile, paying each pew a visit in turn, and lingering longest where the " scran " is thickest.

Far from being a starved-looking skeleton, as church mice are proverbially thought to be, our kirk moose is as round and plump as a tub, and waddles like an over-fed duck. Sam'l, the beadle, is responsible for a great deal of this over-feeding. During the week he pays frequent visits to the church in the course of his duties, and, though he scorns to admit it, never goes without a tit-bit of cheese in his pocket.

.   .   .   .

Sunday is the kirk moose's big day. As soon as he hears the ding-dong of the bells, he preens himself ready for action. He has enough gumption to keep out of Sam'l's way, while he makes his dignified march up the pulpit stairs with the Book, but once that ceremony is over, he is free to embark on his plan of campaign.

There are some pews he knows by instinct to avoid. He is not partial to Mrs. Macnab's elastic-sided boots any more than she is flattered by a visit from him. Indeed, in the days before we learnt to accept the kirk moose as part of the Sabbath routine, there were whiles ungodly skirls to be heard in the middle of a prayer, as the creature playfully sank his claws into a protesting ankle. Now he has found wisdom with the years, and knows at which pews he is likely to find the best hospitality.

The kirk moose has his fads and fancies. He turns up his nose at a cough-drop or an extra-strong. A half-sucked pan-drop is no use for immediate consumption, but it can be rolled towards his hide-out near the pulpit stairs, and stored up to eke out his through-the-week menu. When all else fails, he is not above having a chew at a hymn-book and—perhaps out of spite—has a particular fancy for Mrs. Macnab's, which is now looking decidedly " the waur o' the wear."

There are occasions during the service when the kirk moose tries to mount the pulpit stairs to visit the Minister, but he is sternly brought to heel by Sam'l, who will indulge him in many ways, but not in this. As he says : " We're no' wantin' to hear *you* preach, so ye maun bide doon here amang the rest o' the congregation."

. . . .

The kirk moose seems by now to have the order of service off by heart. The discourse seems to weary him, and several other members of the congregation. Sometimes he has a " dover " ; at other times he runs races up and down the aisle to the great delight of the children. Now and again he climbs up on to a book board, and gives a very able gymnastic display, and in between his frolics, he whisks off at intervals to visit Sam'l, who beams or frowns at him according to his behaviour, and admonishes him in a whisper to " sit doon, man, an' behave like a Christian."

The kirk moose lets out a sigh of relief when he sees the Minister spreading his arms for the benediction. He bows his head meekly until the words are said, then, with a whisk of his tail, he gives a hop-skip-and-jump and scampers off to the shelter of his home.

But when the kirk has scaled, there is little doubt that he emerges again on a mopping-up expedition, and takes charge of any pan-drop or crumb he has missed. Then, when he has gathered his hoard for the week, he is free to leap up the forbidden stairs to have a post-prandial nap in the pulpit, with the satisfied feeling that he has earned his day of rest.

THE MOOSE

Hae ye a moose in the hoose ?
There's ane in mine,
An' fine
I ken the scutter o' his feet
As he comes stottin' oot to eat.

Hae ye a hairt as hard as stane ?
The neibors say I'm daft,
Mine's saft,
For aye I feed the stervin' wee bit beast
Wi' crumbs frae ma ain feast.

Hae ye a froon for folk like me ?
Nae doot wi' times sae thrang
It's wrang.
But, och ! in war or peace it's unco croose
To hae a frien'ly moose aboot the hoose.

Mrs McTosh ilk' Sabbath mornin'
Ye'll find the organ-stool adornin',
Pedallin' awa' wi' siccan zeal
She blisters baith her tae an' heel ;
An', fegs ! the stoor she fairly raises
Stottin' through psalms an' paraphrases.

She bleezes aff at sic a rate
The congregation, shaire as fate,
Fa' far ahint, stechin' an' groanin',
An' reach *Amen* wi' muckle moanin'
Lang efter *she* has skeltered hame.
(The preacher boos his heid in shame).

Syne back she sits, sooplin' her shanks.
The deived kirk-moose comes oot wi' thanks
To keek for pandrops in a pew,
But jouks awa' an' gi'es a grue
When ance again, wi' dreadfu' dunner,
She hammers hard at the *Auld Hunner*.

Fair fretfu' through the sermonisin'
She sits, wi' her impatience risin',
Duntin' her feet upon the flair,
Ettlin' to birl awa' ance mair,
An' goamin' the preacher wi' a glower
To haste an' get his discoorse ower.

Syne fast an' faster flee her feet.
Her last Amen is bad to beat,
An', dod ! it's juist a gamble whether
She'll leave the organ a'thegither.
Eh whowh ; the angels up abune
Maun heave a sigh when ance she's dune.

THE BETHERAL

Wi' stately step an' solemn mien
The poopit stairs he moonts,
An' roon' the kirk wi' mony a glower
The worshippers he coonts.

Wi' carefu' haun's he tak's the Buik
An' sets it i' its place,
Then hirples doon the stairs again,
A prood look on his face.

His auld tail-coat swings east an' wast,
His shirt-front north an' sooth,
As ben he brings the meenister—
A smirk aboot his mooth.

Ay ! meenisters may come an' gang,
An' though they're men o' grace,
It tak's an extra-ordnar' chiel'
To fill a betheral's place.

Granny is firmly convinced that there is only one " Man on the Wireless." The women she dismisses as " a wheen skirlin' blether-skites."

It is the " man " who tells her the latest news, what the weather will be to-morrow (" Dodsakes ! He kens everything ! "), preaches sermons to her on Sundays, speaks in a foreign language when she has turned the knob the wrong way, plays the fiddle, bursts into song, and tells her funny stories.

" Jings, he's weel worth his pound," says Granny admiringly, putting on her spectacles so that she can hear him better. " If onybody airns his siller, it's that man ! "

Granny is greatly impressed with his politeness. " A ceevil cratur', yon," says she, nodding her head in response to his " Good-mornings " and " Good-evenings " ; and, sometimes adding that, " he soonds fine an' chirpy this mornin'," or " he's kind o' rough in the thrapple the day. I doot he'll be hoastin' afore lang."

His versatility leaves her awe-struck. " Losh, he sticks at naethin'," says she, after listening to an account of a Boxing Match, and is greatly relieved when he tells her that he is putting on a gramophone record.

" An' I dinna blame ye, puir man," she says sympathetically. " It'll gi'e ye a chance to ha'e a sit-doon an' a cup o' tea."

When Granny's set is out of order, she is very down in the dumps. " There's something wrang wi' the man on the wireless," she sighs, twirling the knobs in an endeavour to bring him back to life. " He was juist in the middle o' a comic sang when he went clean awa'. I hope the puir sowl hasna ta'en a turn."

And so Granny worries about him until a new battery brings back his voice once more, and she perks up with : " Whisht, there he is, as lairge as life, playin' the organ. Man, it's grand to hear ye again. A pound ? Toots, he's worth dooble ! "

THE UNCTIONEER

Noo, gin ye want a chest o' drawers,
A dresser, or a mangle,
Come doon to Mrs. Tamson's roup
An' see whit ye can wangle.

The unctioneer, auld Geordie Broon,
Gets up an' moonts a table ;
Then doon he knocks the furniture
As fast as he is able.

An' as his hammer birls aboot
Auld Mrs. Tamson's treasures,
It's worth a fortune juist to hear
The wey he tak's their measures.

" The finest i' the countryside,"
Roars he, wi' little favour ;
Be it a creddle or a clock,
His tongue'll never waver.

An' gin ye want to buy a cooch,
Or aiblins juist a ladle,
He's shaire to thraw a pat-lid in,
Or else a bairnie's daidle.

An' tho' ye dinna mean to buy,
Ye'll no' resist his yammer,
For baith your oxters'll be fu'
When Geordie dings his hammer.

THE DAMBROD

The first thing you saw as you went into the cottage
was the dambrod hanging from a hook on the wall;
that is, if Uncle Andrew were out. If he were in, there
was almost sure to be a blank space on the wall, and
the board would be in front of him on the table. Like
as not, his crony, Tamson, would be sitting opposite
him, with his spectacles pushed back on his forehead,
and his whole face wrinkled and tortured with thought.

It was as much as your life was worth to make a
remark when the pair of them were in play. And, indeed,
if you had ventured to warn them that the house was on
fire, Uncle Andrew would only have grunted out a
" Wheesht ! "

Sometimes they would sit for half-an-hour on end,
neither speaking, moving, nor altering their expressions.
When a move was made, it was as momentous as if a
bomb had fallen, yet it was only the prelude to another
long silence.

Even the cat went to sleep, the fire died out, and the
kettle stopped singing. The clock seemed to tick more
gently, as if holding its breath, and when a knock came
to the door, it was like an explosion, but, nevertheless,
an explosion which the players ignored.

So absorbed were they that they seemed out of reach,
beyond contact. There was no drawing them back

until the game was finished. Uncle Andrew was not the same genial man who sang to us about the " Bonnie Hoose o' Airlie " ; he was a stranger held in the thrall of the dambrod. And Tamson was no longer the cheerful, whistling Postman ; he was as unreal as the cow that jumped over the moon.

When at last the board was cleared, there was the sense of relief that one feels when the Preacher says " Amen " at the end of a long, dull sermon. The tension was instantly relaxed. The cat woke up and became playful, the fire flickered into life, the kettle sang, and the clock tick-tocked merrily. The two cronies, the one smirking over his victory, and the other striving to conceal his disappointment, stretched out their cramped limbs and lit their pipes. An air of normality returned to the kitchen. They were human once more.

But the game was not done ; far from it. It had to be played over again in retrospect, before the dambrod was hung back on its hook on the wall, but this time more cheerfully, for there were no silences. Rather did the air become loud with fist-thumpings and noisy recriminations. Uncle Andrew might have won the game, but Tamson could always put forth sound reasons why the honours should have fallen to him. Hammer and tongs, they fought it out, while the kitchen, so silent before, boomed with noise ; the kettle boiled over, and the clock chapped the hour.

At last, when all their arguments were worn thin, Uncle Andrew took up the dambrod, dusted it carefully, and returned it to the hook on the wall. It settled back against the wallpaper, as if thankful that the strife was over, yet knowing that its respite would be brief.

Uncle Andrew and Tamson would smoke on for a while, discussing such commonplace topics as the crops ;

but, ever and anon, their eyes would turn to the dambrod and they would be off again. At the chap of ten, Tamson stretched himself, and made for the door. He looked back, not at Uncle Andrew, but at the dambrod, and said : " I'll be seein' ye the morn's nicht."

" Ay," Uncle Andrew would grunt, also with his eyes on the dambrod ; " we'll have her doon again the morn."

THE DAMBROD

Auld Dawvid, ower the dambrod droopin',
Wi' specs askew an' shouthers stoopin',
Aft' scarts his heid,
Gies whiles a grunt an' whiles a grue,
Cautious in case a shot he'll rue
An' lose the lead.

His weary rival, gantin' sair,
Waits on his turn an' dunts the flair
Wi' shauchlin' shoon ;
Thinkin' : " Eh whowh ! I'm cornered noo ! "
An' syne, wi' sweet upon his broo,
Yields up a croon.

The guidwife, ettlin' for a crack,
Is forced to keep her clashes back,
For fear o' froons ;
An' e'en the clock daur hardly chap,
The cat lies listless in her lap,
Cravin' nae boons.

But tho' he tak's his pleesures sair,
Dodsakes ! auld Dawvid wadna care
For wealth an' fame,
Nor swap the dambrod for a croon,
For noo, wi' a triumphant soon',
He's gained the game.

SOLEMN OCCASION

It is a solemn occasion when the ben-end fire is lit.
The lum, unaccustomed to the sudden heat, sends down
whiffs of smoke, (and, at times, a starling's nest), and
Aunt Jessie is in a frenzy, lest her plush chairs will suffer.

They, along with most of the contents of the ben-end,
have a history that dates back to the time of her " doon-
sittin'," and must all be treasured in consequence, even
though they have long outlived their early glories.

For some strange reason, neither Aunt Jessie nor
Uncle Andrew can walk naturally across the faded
stretch of ben-end carpet. Aunt Jessie traverses it on
tip-toe, but Uncle Andrew seems to think it safer to
cross it on his heels.

Luckily the occasions on which they need to adopt
this peculiar method of perambulation are so few that
the neighbours, on seeing smoke arising from the
chimney, remark : " Dodsakes, there maun be something
byordnar' gaun on upbye. The ben-end lum's reekin'."

Uncle Andrew is proud of the ben-end as a spectacle,
but he is not half the man there that he is in the kitchen.

He looks ill at ease, finds himself speaking " fine,"
using unfamiliar phrases, and sitting in an unrelaxed
attitude in front of the brass fender where, like the dove,
he can find no rest for the sole of his foot.

In vain does he look for a suitable place to knock the dottle from his pipe; he would never dream of reading his paper in such perjinct surroundings, and it would be sacrilege even to breathe the word " dambrod " in the ben-end.

" Verra braw," he admits, admiring the roses on the wallpaper, and the curtains tied back with ribbon, and before long he hurries back on his heels to the sanctuary of the kitchen.

Aunt Jessie lingers longer. She sits bolt upright on one of her plush chairs, and gazes round at her treasures, one by one.

The picture of herself and Uncle Andrew, on their Wedding Day, seems very remote. Surely she never had a waist like that, nor Uncle Andrew such a magnificent moustache.

Her eyes stray to the brass pot, containing the aspidistra (a cutting from her Mother's) and from there to the old calendar, which seems to have merged into the roses on the wallpaper, and made a pattern for itself there.

Mentally, she associates every object with the person who gave it to her, or the roup at which she and Uncle Andrew bought it, and as she sits there the ben-end becomes peopled with old friends and scenes from the past.

Yet—though she never admits it—Aunt Jessie is as ill at ease in the ben-end as Uncle Andrew. There is no settling down by the fire with her darning-basket.

There is no swey on which to hang a singing kettle, no hob for the teapot; no cat at her feet. (Having once peeped round the door, Fluffy gives a startled miew, and beats a hasty retreat to the comforts of the kitchen rug.)

It is a relief to Aunt Jessie when Uncle Andrew comes in on his heels to say : " There's a bleezin' fire in the kitchen, an' the kettle's on the boil. C'wa' ben, wumman."

Aunt Jessie rises from her plush chair, gives a final glance round the room, and tip-toes to the door.

In the kitchen, Aunt Jessie and Uncle Andrew put their slippered feet on the fender, proud to know that they have a ben-end, but thankful that they have snecked the door on it.

THE DOMINIE

Wi' spectacles abune his nose,
The tawse atween his haun's,
The dominie, wi' fearsome froon,
Aside the blackboard staun's.

" Noo, hear to me, ye donnert loons ! "
Cries he, wi' wrathfu' glower,
As intil ilka timmer heid
He knocks the lairnin' ower.

Frae morn till nicht he warstles on,
His tawse an' tongue ne'er still,
Until o' skelps an' lesson-buiks
The scholars hae their fill.

But though his tongue wad clip a cloot,
His tawse flee a' the airts,
The dominie's a canny chiel'
To ilka lad o' pairts.

An' mony bless his helpin' haun'
That's guided them to fame ;
For though his tawse is unco hard,
His hairt is no' the same.

THE BEN-END

Noo, ben the hoose i' solemn gloom
You'll find the parlour-end,
Wi' cushioned sates, an' ornaments
An' flooers that winna bend.

The clock upon the mantelshelf
Has never chapped the hoor ;
The sideboard, wi' its cheeny dugs,
Is covered ower wi' stoor.

The wundda's steekit tap an' tae,
The fire thraws oot nae lowe ;
An aspidistra, auld an' teuch,
Hings doon its thirsty pow.

An' a' is braw, wi' fancy rugs
An' carpets on the flair,
Wi' muckle pictur's on the wa',
An' e'en an easy-chair.

But tho' a ben-end we can boast
Within oor humble hoose,
I' lanesome splendour it maun bide—
The kitchen-end's mair croose.

CAGED

Ye're sae kind to me,
But I wush't I was free
To try oot ma wings that are ettlin' for flight ;
Yet ye feed me sae weel
That I canna but feel
I maun chirp to your biddin' frae mornin' till night.

But e'en while I eat
Some denty wee treat
I'd raither be oot scartin' worms for ma meals ;
Still, I'll sing gin ye please
Tho' it gies me nae ease,
For hoo can ye ken hoo a prisoner feels ?

LITTLE OLD LADY

Granny has lived through many Wars. Her mind
is somewhat blurred by now, so that she talks, even of
the Battle of Bannockburn, as though she had relations
fighting on both sides. She has only a very vague
notion of who the contestants of the latest struggle
are, and speaks of " Yon Napoleon " with great contempt.

Granny lives in the little lodge-house at the foot of
the village, and sits at the window in Summer, and the
ingle-nook in Winter. When she was young and spry,
she used to go out to open the big gates, and bob to
the Laird and his Lady, as they rattled through in their

carriage. But now that the " pains " have gripped her, she can only hirple about the kitchen, and watch the world go by through her little window.

Every day, she goes through various rites, the chief of which is making her bed, a ceremony which lasts her nearly an hour.

" I maun do it ma ain way," she says stubbornly, and will allow no one to help her. Her only assistant is a stout stick, which she uses when smoothing down the patchwork quilt.

Often she goes into what she terms a " dwam " when a sight of some patch in the quilt rakes up old memories and sends her thoughts back to scenes which she thought long forgotten.

Her next task is to dust the mantel-piece, where her china dogs sit in a solemn row. But her eyesight is poor, and she is continually breaking the dogs, and having them replaced by her sympathetic " grand-children."

Although she wears spectacles, they are of little value to her eyesight, for, as she proudly tells us : " They belanged to ma faither." It is no use trying to induce her to get new ones. " What was guid eneuch for ma faither's guid eneuch for me," is her opinion.

When she has redd up the kitchen, she puts on her mutch, and her " hug-me-tight " and sits down at the window, or at the fire. From the hidden " pooch " in her voluminous black skirt, she brings forth a pandrop, and sits waiting for visitors to arrive.

Granny is fond of company, and is seldom without it, for her pawky ways have made her the most popular figure in the village. The Minister, who often drops into the lodge-house, declares that he gets many of the ideas for his sermons from the old lady, to whom he is just a " bit callant " to be treated with scant ceremony.

Her large family of " grandchildren " seldom come empty-handed but, as Granny has strict ideas of independence, she will accept nothing offhand. Various manoeuvres, however, take place behind her back, and her wall press is kept well stocked, and she seldom needs to buy provisions for herself.

As she claims to be able to " read the cups " every visitor must submit to having her fortune told. Unfortunately, Granny's memory has failed so badly that she forgets which of her " grandchildren " are married, and predicts " a lad wi' gowd hair an' siller i' his pooch " for a comfortably married woman with a large family.

Granny also tells us that she had a " voice " when she was young, and is fond of quavering out her old favourites when she can get anyone to listen. Thinking it would please her, the Minister brought her a wireless set one day, but, after listening to it for a few minutes, she told him to " tak' that heathenish thing awa'. I canna mak' heid nor tail o' sic foreign blethers."

The Minister hastened to assure her that it was only an Englishman speaking. " Weel," said Granny in disgust, " that's shairly foreign eneuch."

Now that the War has come, Granny insists on doing her bit. This takes the form of " knittin' for the sodgers." Day after day, she sits throppling away at a strange garment which she calls a " gravat."

" Ay," says she, as she pops another pandrop into her mouth, " I maun do ma bit for auld Queen Victoria."

THE MENDIN'

Whiles I wad watch ma Granny's powe
Nid-noddin' in the lamp-lit lowe
Abune her steeks ;
Wi' twa-three preens preed in her mou',
Her spectacles aboot her broo,
Mendin' ma breeks.

She'd lay a duddy cloutie doon,
Her face wad wrinkle in a froon,
An' syne she'd grummle :
" Sic callants' clyters ye maun hae
To mak' *this* mischief in ae day !
What gaur'd ye tummle ? "

But fine I kent she wadna girn,
Sae, playin' peevers wi' the pirn,
I tell't ma story ;
O' hoo I'd focht wi' giants three,
Scaled wa's an' dykes an' sclim'd a tree,
To fame an' glory.

She'd rax the shears, say : " Mexty me !
Ye're unco bold for ane sae wee ;
Teuch as a tyke !
Ay, heroes hae some darin' ways,
But maun they always tear their claes,
Speelin' a dyke ? "

Hoots, Granny, tho' ye tried to flicht,
Ye liked thae canty cracks at nicht,
If I'm no' wrang ;
An' as ye warstled owre the steeks,
Felt pleased that I had torn ma breeks,
An' kept ye thrang.

THOUGHTS IN CHURCH

Eh whowh ; I'll never find ma text
An' then ma Granny'll be vexed ;
I maunna fussle ower the Book ;
He micht hae made it *Psalms* or *Luke*,
But *Malachi* fair gaurs me grue ;
I wonder if it's *Auld* or *New* ?
Puir Mrs. Broon ! she's gantin' sair.
The meenister looks queer up there
Wavin' his airms an' roarin' lood.
I wonder if he's awfu' good ?
There's still nae sign o' *Malachi* ;
I'd better hae anither try.
Jings ! Geordie's winkin' frae his pew ;
I'd like a peppermint to chew.
Oh dear ! I wush that we were oot ;
I'd like to gang an' guddle troot.
Guidsakes ! here's *Malachi* at last,
An' noo the sermon's nearly past.
I ken that I'm an awfu' sinner,
But, och ! I'm ettlin' for ma dinner.

THE AULD STANE

Ilk' Sabbath when the kirk has skailed
An' doucer fowk gane hame,
Amang the kirkyaird stanes I bide
To read a moss-grown name.

In lanesome solitude he lies,
A lang-forgotten chiel' ;
An' though his face I ne'er can see,
I ken his name fu' weel.

For there ma namesake sleeps i' peace,
Lang-rested, lang-forgot ;
An' noo ma ain bit day's near dune
I sune maun share his lot.

But when at last the trumpet soonds
An' I've laid doon ma load,
I'll hae a frien' to gie a haund
An' help me on the road.

BIG BELLA THE BONDAGER

Big Bella, who looks after the animals, helps with the harvest, and even, on occasions, follows the plough, has become a kind of mascot at The Mains where she " works oot." She is a large, broad woman with a loud voice, and the rolling gait of Jolly Jack Tars and farm labourers. Essentially a creature of the soil, she needs plenty of space to move about in, and scorns those who lead a soft indoor life, devoting themselves to what she terms, " Fancy-work and sic-like trash."

Bella, who also scorns the modern land-girl's craze for " troosers," has a uniform peculiar to herself. It consists of an old black skirt, which she kilts up over a striped petticoat, and a hug-me-tight type of blouse. Her wild head is crowned by a large straw hat, which has become a landmark in the district, where it is known as " Bella's Basher." On her sturdy legs she wears corduroy leggings, while her feet are encased in tackety boots with no nonsense about them.

Although she has many activities on the farm, Bella's chief preoccupation is with the animals. Indeed, as her fellow-workers crudely put it : " Big Bella's heid's fou' o' beasts."

She treats them in a hail-fellow-well-met manner, wasting no time in fondling them, but talking to them as casually as if they were human beings.

" An' whit for no' ? " she defends herself, " seein' they've got a hantle mair gumption in their heids than a wheen fowk I could mention ! "

When she goes to the byre in the early morning, Bella invariably greets Jinnit, the cow, with remarks about the weather.

" Ay, it's geyan snell this mornin'," she will say, taking off her basher, preparatory to burying her head in the cow's flank while she milks. " I doot there's a whuff o' snaw i' the air. Noo then, Jinnit, haud ower there, an' staund still, for I've nae time to waste. I'm gaun oot to the tattie-howkin' as sune as I'm through wi' the beasts."

The animals seem to appreciate these little pleasantries, and are always ready to do her bidding, and to run to her as soon as they hear her voice.

Big Bella has no undertones. Her loud remarks are heard all over the farm, as she scolds the hens for not having laid, or advises the pigs to : " Hae some mainners an' dinna slaister sae muckle, or I'll gi'e ye a skelpin' whaur it hurts maist."

All the hands on the farm have a wholesome respect for the bondager, mingled with not a little fear. In the harvest-field, or when they are singling turnips, Big Bella always shows up the slackers. She never tires, and shows a loud contempt for those who do, referring to them scornfully, as : " Peelie-wally ploiterers."

Bella invariably undertakes the task of building the corn stacks, for none of the men can work as neatly and swiftly as she can. She balances on top of the stack, her basher pushed rakishly on the back of her head, and catches stook after stook in her brawny arms. All the time, she adjures the men in a loud voice to: "Get a move on, or I'll be up here for the duration. It's peevers ye should be playin' wi', no' corn-stooks."

Wee Wullie, the herd, who is the exact antithesis of her, has a profound admiration for Bella, and has many a time tried to pluck up courage to ask her to name the day. But Bella treats the little shepherd with a kind of amused contempt and says: "I'd as sune tackle a mitherless lamb ony day as that shauchlin' wee sowl." Yet she defends him from the raillery of the other men, and is always ready to give him a hand with his flock, lifting sheep in her sturdy arms when he himself is at a loss how to tackle them. At clipping times, she takes her turn at the shearing, and when the sheep need dipping, Wee Wullie finds her a valuable assistant.

"Hoots ay, I ha'e to gi'e him a haund," she remarks; "If it wasna' for me the wee cratur' wad gang tapsulteerie in amang the sheep an' be drooned as like as no'."

Big Bella has another side to her character when she is off duty. No local function is complete without her, for in spite of her weight and size, she is surprisingly light on her feet and is never at a loss for partners for "Corn Riggs" or "Drops o' Brandy." She hoochs and twirls her way through the dances with great gusto, birling her less brawny partners off their feet, and boisterously egging on the fiddler to play faster. "There's naebody like Big Bella for raisin' the stoor at the jiggin'," is a byeword in the district.

But no matter how long the dance lasts, or how strenuous have been her activities, Bella is never late in her early-morning visit to Jinnit, the cow, to whom she relates, as a matter of course, the high-lights of the evening's entertainment.

"Jings, yon was a fine ploy last nicht, Jinnit," she says, as the milk stots down into the pail. "I had them a' flattened oot at the Lancers. Ye should ha'e seen Wee Wullie's face when I birled him aff his feet ! Noo then, keep your tail to yersel', ma wumman, or ye'll no ha'e your sorrows to seek."

It is at the annual kirn or harvest-home, however, that Big Bella enjoys herself most of all. It is held in the granary above the byre, and here, after their long toil in the harvest-field, the workers and their friends reap their reward in a night of such fast and furious frolic that even the docile Jinnit down below, raises her voice in protest.

The high-spot of the entertainment comes when Big Bella takes the floor to "oblige" with the song she always sings at the kirn. It is "The Lum Hat," rendered in a deep voice which would do justice to a *basso profundo*. The song usually ends in a duet between Bella and Jinnit, for the cow, hearing the well-known voice, raises her own in greeting, or it may be disapprobation. Between verses, Bella will roar : "Haud your tongue, Jinnit, or I'll sort ye i' the mornin'," and in spite of all opposition perseveres to the end.

Whether at the kirn or in the harvest-field, yoking the great Clydesdales or "weirin'" the sheep for Wee Wullie, Big Bella throws herself into the business of the moment with all the dynamic energy of her large frame. As she admits : "I'll never be an ornament, so I micht as well be usefu'." And so she clumps her way about the farm, as sturdy and reliable as the dry-stane dykes that she herself has helped to build.

23

THE BONDAGER

Auld Mirren, teuch as ony tyke,
Can mend a pleuch or big a dyke,
Muck oot the byre, wi' little steerie,
Or oxter stooks when ithers weary.

She feeds the hens an' milks the coos,
Cairts muckle pails oot to the soos ;
An' aft wi' beasts ye'll hear her blether
On siclike subjects as the weather.

She stramps aboot in muckle buits,
Wi' leggin's rowed aboot her cuits ;
Roars oot her orders to the cattle
Like ony colonel in a battle.

Whit tho' her tongue wad clip a cloot,
An' hauflins flee when she's aboot ?
The beasties thole the randy's roarin'
An' do her biddin', fair adorin'.

There's little lairnin' i' her heid ;
The Buik is a' she's time to read,
But Mirren's nearer faur to Natur'
Than ony clever-heided cratur'.

THE VILLAGE BOBBY

Rubbert the Bobby still has high hopes of finding a
desperate band of gangsters in our peaceful village, or
of tracking down a blood-stained murderer, in spite of

the fact that his nearest approach to crime has been in prosecuting Mrs. Macnab when her lum went on fire— an act which he has lived to regret bitterly, for she has made his life nothing but a misery ever since. There has not even been an accident at the cross-roads within living memory (nor is there likely to be, since the day's traffic seldom exceeds a cadger's van and a couple of bicycles), and the idea of burgling each other's houses never seems to occur to the villagers, who have also an annoying habit of dying peacefully in their beds of old age.

"It's eneuch to gaur ye tak' to crime yersel'," grumbles Rubbert, laying aside his unused baton and turning for consolation to a blood-thirsty Detective story. "Eh, whowh, if only I had a beat in Chicago ! They say there's a throat cut there every meenit o' the day."

Every morning he emerges hopefully from the Police Station—as his cottage is officially called—dressed in his regulation garb, with his baton at the ready, his notebook and pencil in his hand, and various secret weapons stowed about his person. Alert for clues, and anxious to encounter a guilty criminal, he pompously parades the village street, turning a deaf ear to Mrs. Macnab's snorts of derision, and admonishing the few straggling school-bairns to : "Move alang there, an' dinna cause an obstruction i' the traffic."

Even the local dogs are subjected to "offeecial" orders, but seem so little awed by his dignified presence that they snap at his ankles as if he were an ordinary man, and remain unmoved by his threats to "ha'e the law on them." Indeed, Mrs. Macnab's mongrel, no doubt coerced by its mistress, has taken such a spite at him that it is not unusual to see Rubbert ignominiously scuttling back to the Police Station with the dog snapping ferociously at his heels.

The Bobby's bitterest disappointment is that the outhouse reserved for a jail has not once been occupied, even by a stray vagrant, let alone by the hordes of desperadoes he has many a time locked up in his imagination. After weary years of waiting, he has at last converted it into a coal-house, and his nightly visits to the " kitty " are taken in company of a coal-scuttle instead of a cat-o'-nine-tails.

In spite of the scarcity of crime, Rubbert manages to fill page after page of his notebook in strange caligraphy, which consists chiefly of reporting stray cattle, the outbreak of foot-and-mouth disease, and the fact that he has acted as witness at various " sheep-dippin's " At the latter ceremony, the local shepherds—and especially Gillies of the Knowe—are by no means appreciative of his presence ; for, after making as many notes as if he were tracking down Public Enemy Number One, he has an annoying habit of meddling with the task in hand.

" Can ye no' mind your ain business ? " cried Gillies in exasperation one day. " I've a guid mind to dook ye in the dipper yersel'."

" I'm only offerin' ye soond advice," said the Bobby, in an aggrieved voice. " Ye're no' gaun aboot it in the richt wey. Ye've got the beasts gliffed oot their wuts. Put them in canny-like, an' they'll be as happy as linties."

" Fancy that ! " scoffed Gillies. " Weel, it's no' for the likes o' me to contradict the law. Mebbe ye'd like to ha'e a shot yersel' ? "

" Dod ! Whit for no' ? " said Rubbert, stowing away his notebook, and advancing nearer to the dipper. " A polisman's as weel to try his hand at everything."

" Juist so ! " Gillies was biding his time. " Whit aboot stertin' on this ane ? " He indicated a meek-looking member of the flock, which, nevertheless, was a randy, as the shepherd well knew.

" Richt ! " said Rubbert, ready for action. " Come on, beastie. A canny shove an' it'll sune be a' ower. Ye're gaun to enjoy this."

But the sheep thought otherwise, for when Rubbert laid a persuasive hand on its woolly coat, it put down its head and butted him soundly.

Gillies looked on with satisfaction. " Man," said he, dryly, " I'm admirin' your methods."

The Bobby grunted, and then addressed the sheep sternly : " Nane o' your nonsense, noo ! I'm daein' this for your ain guid, if ye only kent it ! "

His remarks were greeted by another bout of boxing. Rubbert grew impatient. " Ye savage brute ! " he roared. " I'll ha'e the law on ye for this," and, seizing the sheep, he tried to heave it nearer to the edge. But the randy was in form ; savagely it hurled itself against the Bobby, and before he could step aside to safety, he was rushed into the dipper, the sheep staggering in after him with a loud splash.

Since then Rubbert, his note-book stained with sheep-dip to remind him of his Waterloo, has been unusually subdued at such ceremonies, and takes care to stand at a safe distance from the dipper.

At the outbreak of War, his hopes ran so high that he moved his coal to one side of the " jail " to make room for the spies he hoped to capture. But, apart from the advent of Peerie, the evacuee (who has come to stay with Mrs. Macnab for the sole purpose, it would seem, of tormenting the life out of the Bobby, who considers him a mixture of Al Capone, Hitler, and the

27

Devil) the war has brought no increase of crime to the village. In fact, so reluctant is the Gestapo to make its appearance, and so sweart are aeroplanes to crash in Rubbert's back-yard, that he has thought seriously of " chuckin' in ma baton an' jinin' the Commandos."

Certainly Peerie has enlivened things a little by creating a gang of four or five kindred spirits, who call themselves " The Dare-devils," and who meet in Mrs. Macnab's coal-house to plan their desperate adventures. Armed with water-pistols and bows and arrows, they follow their intrepid leader through thick and thin, their chief delight being in jouking the Bobby, while, at the same time, bombarding him with missiles from behind a dyke.

Though Rubbert has had to start a new notebook in which to record their misdeeds, he has never succeeded in catching them red-handed, nor is he likely to, since Peerie is as wily as a fox, and can easily outdistance him, both in speed and wit.

The Bobby suffered his greatest indignity at the hands of the gang when he " lost " his baton, which he had left unguarded one day when he was hurriedly summoned by a small boy to : " Come quick, for ony favour. There's a murder gaun on at the Knowe." In a great state of excitement, Rubbert rushed madly to the scene of crime, where he discovered Gillies in the act of killing a pig, and none too pleased to see his adversary at such a crucial moment.

Returning, dejected, to the " Police Station," Rubbert made the discovery that his baton was gone, and after spending many frenzied hours searching for it, found that a grubby piece of paper had been thrust beneath his door.

The message read : " If you want your batton,

look below the cole in the kitty.   The Dare-devils."

Fuming with rage, Rubbert searched among the coal, discovering not his baton, but another message, this time inserted in an old can, and reading : " Soled again. Try lookin' in the gardin among the carots."

One clue led to another, and it was not until Rubbert was nearly exhausted with fury and hard work that he eventually found the missing treasure in " a whole in the dike doon by the cross-rods."

Storming with anger, he bearded the leader of " The Dare-devils " in his strong-hold in Mrs. Macnab's kitchen but was non-plussed by Peerie's innocence and Mrs. Macnab's threats to " sort him."

There was nothing for it, but to return to the " Police Station," the loser of the day, and add yet another black mark against Peerie in his note-book.

Some day, however, Rubbert is convinced that he will come into his own, and that an account of his daring deeds will figure (with a photograph) in all the newspapers. For, as he says : " Shairly somebody'll murder somebody if I wait lang eneuch ; an' if no', dang it, I'll dae't masel'."

THE BOBBY

Auld Rubbert, though his feet are flat,
Skites up the street like ony cat,
His whustle ready at the toot,
Hopin' a murder to find oot,
An' thinkin' it's an awfu' pity
He's nabbit naebody for the kitty.

To sort the traffic aye he likes,
(A cuddy-cairt an' twa-three bikes),
An' waves his airms aboot like flails
That e'en the weemen wi' their pails
Maun wait his pleesure at the crossin',
Sae fond is Rubbert o' his bossin' !

Hech ! hoo he's ettlin' for a case !
There's never ony in the place,
Although, to gie him his desire,
We sometimes set a lum on fire ;
An' then to hear his whustle bummin'
Ye'd think the Day o' Judgment comin'.

But, though he kens it's faur frae richt
When poachin' bodies roam by nicht,
Aiblins he'll look the ither airt
(For Rubbert has a kindly hairt)—
An' whiles ablow his oxter cuddled
Ye'll find a fush that *he* has guddled !

THE KIRK PILLAR

Ilk' Sabbath at the auld kirk door
The elder stands an' keeps the score ;
An' aye his watchfu' een are lookin'
For fowk wha try to do some joukin'.

Wi' dignity that nane can bate
He'll froon upon a chiel wha's late ;
An' as the bells begude their dunner
He'll saftly whustle the Auld Hunner.

A pillar o' the kirk he stands,
His Sabbath lum hat i' his hands ;
But i' his pooch, there's nae denyin'
Ye'll find a sinfu' pandrop lyin'.

THE WEE DOCTOR

One of the outstanding figures to be seen at Country Fairs in days gone by was a diminutive, red-nosed gentleman, known popularly as " the wee doctor."

The most professional thing about him was his " black bag," which was almost as big as himself, and which could produce as many surprise items as a lucky bag.

" The wee doctor " established himself in a prominent part of the fairground, mounted himself on a wooden stand—else he would never have been seen at all—and set out to attract an audience by the eloquence of his patter.

The very sight of him in his " professional " dress, which consisted of a tail-coat much too big, and a pair of breeches much too tight, with a tall hat which, on occasion, swamped his face altogether, was enough to lure the crowd, even from the noisy attractions of the circus, or the delights of the ginger-bread stalls. They clustered round him, demanding to know " whit ' the wee doctor ' had in his black bag," and if he had " found oot a cure for wudden legs."

The " doctor " took these good-natured sallies in the spirit in which they were offered, beamed on the crowd, and then burst forth into his inaugural address.

" Weel, I'm glad to be back wi' ye, frien's," he began briskly, " an' to see ye a' sae cheery, tho' there's

31

ane or two o' ye kind o' peely-wally looking, but a sowp o' ma medicine 'll put ye richt. Noo, if ony o' ye ha'e pains i' the stomach, corns on the taes, spots afore the een, chilblains, toothache, varicose veins, or floatin' kidneys, just say the word an' I'll sort ye in two shakes o' a coo's tail."

This speech was greeted with loud cries of " Guid for the wee doctor ! Show us whit's in the black bag."

At this encouragement, the " doctor " would dive into his bag, fumble about for a time, and bring forth a packet of his celebrated " Pills for a' Occasions."

" Ye can sook them or chew them or swallow them hale," was his slogan. " Nae maitter whaur your pain is, ma pills'll find it oot. Wha's for a box ? A penny a time."

" The wee doctor " never lacked customers. With great rapidity, he handed out his home-made pills, and transferred the coins to the pocket of his tail-coat until he jingled like a thrifty with every gesture he made.

Occasionally, to fortify himself, he took draughts from a suspicious-looking black bottle which he produced from his bag, and which he explained away as " pheesic for his hoast." It was noted that it had also a very cheering effect on him, and that after imbibing he found it difficult to keep his stance.

Indeed he often tumbled off the platform in amongst his audience, and had to be set up on his feet again.

Although he had many requests for samples of the medicine from the black bottle, the " doctor " watched over it zealously, and produced instead several flasks of coloured liquid which he described as his " special mixture—a grand staund-by for the cauld. Ye can swallow it, rub it on your chest, or polish the furniture wi't."

Occasionally " the wee doctor," wearied of his salesmanship, shut up shop for the moment, and went off to indulge one of his favourite passions, which was a " hurl " on the round-a-bouts. As the tinny music blared out, he hung precariously to a painted horse, and bobbed up and down with a cherubic smile on his face, while the money jingled in his pocket, and his tall hat fell unheeded among the crowd who gathered round to cheer his progress.

Back once more to his professional duties, he next did a roaring trade in cough candy made from a secret recipe of his own, and a great favourite among the country folk, who bought it in penny pokes, and began to eat it on the spot, whether they were subject to " hoasts " or not.

" A penny a poke," cried " the wee doctor." " Sook it i' the kirk, and I'll wager it'll warm up the driechiest discoorse."

Believing that variety is the spice of life, the " doctor " did not confine his medical duties to selling pills. After disposing of the last poke of cough candy, he fixed a pair of spectacles firmly on his nose, looked solemnly round at his audience, and then produced a formidable pair of pliers from his black bag.

" Noo, then," he began, waving the pliers ominously above his head, " onybody wi' gumboils or sair teeth juist step up an' I'll sort them. Saxpence a time."

This generous offer seldom produced a customer, and indeed it was only in cases of extreme emergency, when teeth were unbearably " sair " that the pliers were brought into use, and a " painless " operation performed. When this happened, the yells of the victim were so loud that the " doctor " was forced to put away his pliers in a hurry, and produce a new diversion to pacify the crowd.

Had the occasion arisen, however, there was no doubt that he would have tackled a major operation on the spot.

His final performance took the form of " Private Consultations " at sixpence a time. By now, too tired and unsteady to stand on his feet, he sat down on his platform.

Country wives came up to him with long tales of their complaints, for which he always had a remedy in his black bag. He produced bundles of herbs and strange potions, bandaged up " sair thoombs," gave endless advice, and fortified himself with liberal swigs from his own private medicine bottle.

At length, when both he and the contents of the black bag were exhausted, he finally shut up shop, and went off to have a last " hurl " on the round-a-bouts. As he said : " Even a doctor maun ha'e his divairsion."

THE DOCTOR

Auld Doctor Broon, a man o' micht,
Mak's a' oor stoonds an' stechin's richt ;
O' pills an' potions he's the maister,
An' ocht he'll mend wi' stickin'-plaister.

His pooches teem wi' this an' that,
He cairries cough-draps i' his hat ;
An' aft, as on his roonds he'll bustle,
Ye'll hear his cheerfu', timmer whustle.

On mony a cauldrife nicht an' snell
He'll sclim ower snawy drift or fell
To see some wife wha thinks she's deein',
An' find the daftlike body's leein'.

But gin the pain's in heid or wame,
He leaves a bottle juist the same ;
Fu' weel he kens the fowk it pleases,
Altho' it michtna cure their sneezes.

To hae the Doctor by their side
Is somethin' they can tell wi' pride ;
For aye he's canty, croose, an' ceevil—
An' whiles contrives to cheat the Deevil.

PAVEMENT ARTIST

Old Rembrandt, who is practically the corner-stone
of our street, has plied his trade on the same bit of
pavement for more years than we can recall. His
drawings, never of the best, are growing somewhat
shaky now, but he still takes infinite pains and pride in
them and fancies they are " as guid as ony in the Royal
Academy."

In keeping with his artistic profession, Rembrandt
has a long beard that sometimes dangles on the pavement, as he bends forward to add another uncertain
stroke to one of his masterpieces. He is a little man,
bent and battered, but with a spirit that remains unbeaten
and a faith in his own genius that nothing can dim.

As the pavement has been his studio for so many
years, he has made it as comfortable as possible. He
has a patchwork cushion for his knees, and another for

his back when he leans up against the railings for a surreptitious snooze.

His crayons he keeps in an old tin box which, he is fond of telling, was given him by a famous artist, who stopped to admire his work. And always by his side, sits his mongrel dog, The Laughing Cavalier, who is the subject of many of his drawings, and who has a jaunty way of grinning at passers-by.

The old pavement artist has many "regulars" who stop to admire his portrait gallery. It is they who have called him Rembrandt, and very proud he is to bear the name.

"Yon," he remarks reflectively, "was a man! But, jings, if I'd only had some rale canvas to work on instead o' a cauld pavement, I wad ha'e dune as weel masel'."

As spelling is not his strong point, we often see such tit-bits printed on the pavement as "A Veiw of the Fourth Brige" side by side with a "Portrate of King Gorge." But without such guidance it would be difficult to recognise some of the things he is trying to depict.

Favoured customers who occasionally have their "portrates" drawn need great strength of character, as well as powers of prevarication, to congratulate the artist on what he terms "a speakin' likeness."

Although most of his drawings are done on the pavement, Rembrandt has a museum piece painted on cracked canvas which he deems his master-piece, and which he always sets down in a prominent place. It is, according to its caption, "A Studdy of a Bone," which he has trained The Laughing Cavalier to sniff at as if it were the real thing. Neither the dog nor the passers-by, however, are much impressed by the likeness, but The Laughing Cavalier is too faithful and well trained to show his contempt in public.

Whenever a coin rattles down into the gaping cap that is set beside the portrait gallery, both master and dog show their appreciation to the passers-by. Rembrandt gives a dignified, but not too humble nod, while The Laughing Cavalier rears up on his hind legs, grins amicably, and then bows his thanks. When a generous patron parts with a silver coin, the dog seems to sense the difference and goes through various evolutions, finally " dying for his country " in gratitude.

Rembrandt's most treacherous enemy is the weather, which takes no tent of artistic genius. The sun will shine slyly until the old man has put the last quavering stroke to a " portrate," and then the rain will patter spitefully on to his master-piece and gradually wash it into the gutter.

While the deluge lasts, Rembrandt and his dog take shelter in a nearby close, staring disconsolately out at the rain and thinking, no doubt, of their empty larder. No amount of concentration on " A Studdy of a Bone " will console The Laughing Cavalier, but, fortunately, there are always " regulars " willing to hand out coins, even though they have not the joy of admiring Rembrandt's works of art.

The old man, however, has tried to prepare for rainy days by learning to play the tin whistle. Even The Laughing Cavalier loses his grin when the quavering notes start up and slinks shamefully away until the sun shines again and his master can return to his real art.

Rembrandt has many rivals in nearby streets, and occasionally leaves his " studio " in charge of the dog, so that he can take a daun'er and view their drawings. Most of these drawings he terms " ower fancifu' " and advises them to stick to sunset scenes " an' no fash wi' caricatures o' the Lord Provost." His fellow-artists listen politely to the old man's words of wisdom, but protest vigorously when he demands "a shot wi'" their crayons to illustrate his point.

After viewing their work, he returns to his own site, convinced that no one can rival him in the perfection of his art.

"Ay," says he, patting the grinning dog with satisfaction, "you an' me ha'e the hale o' them beaten. Some day, when I'm hingin' in the Royal Academy, they'll mind hoo I tried to help them to be as guid as masel'."

PAVEMENT ARTIST

Auld Rorie on the pavement sits,
Scartin' his heid to stir his wits ;
Syne, wi' a waesome hoast or twa,
His fummlin' fingers stert to draw.

Is that a ship, or sunset sky ?
The heedless heels gang stottin' by.
Is that a seashore, or is't Spain
He's chalkin' in wi' micht an' main ?

A battered bunnet's waitin' there.
Shairly a copper ye can spare ?
But noo relentless raindraps fa',
An' ships an' Spain are washed awa'.

McTosh is, without doubt, the uncrowned king of our village. He is chief Elder, Special Constable, and " Heid Bummer " at every function from the Kirk Soiree down to the pig-killing. More than that, he runs the local 'bus, which carries mails, passengers, farm implements, and even live-stock to and from the town, ten miles away.

There have been many controversies about the vintage of the 'bus, which has long been known as " The Baneshaker," and which, according to local clashma-clavers, is fastened together with " claes-pegs, safety preens, and bits o' binder-twine."

Some say that it was at one time a city omnibus which, after a series of drastic crashes, had been rescued from the scrapheap. Others aver that it was the original of all 'buses, and as such had served a long and weary sentence before it fell into McTosh's hands.

.   .   .   .

There is no doubt, however, that the Baneshaker must have been a bit of good stuff at one time. How else could it have stood up to McTosh's blitzkrieg methods of changing the gears, skiting round corners on two wheels, reversing casually into dykes and gable-ends, and neglecting to feed it with its due ration of oil and water, and, more often than not, ignoring its need for petrol as well.

" I dinna fash aboot her inside till she sits doon on the road an' winna budge," says McTosh, who never meets trouble half-way. " Then I juist tak' aff her bunnet gi'e her a bit poke here, an' a bit pou' there, an' awa' she stots like a steam-engine."

The Baneshaker certainly sounds like a steam-engine, as she comes rollicking down the village street in the morning. With a jolt that would do credit to a bucking broncho, she comes to a halt at the Post Office, where McTosh descends to collect the mail and to take on passengers.

.   .   .   .

Before he finally sets off, he has to solve a giant jig-saw puzzle. The Baneshaker groans as Mrs. McWhirter lowers her bulk into a corner seat, creaks when McTosh heaves in a sack of potatoes, and another containing a young calf, heels over to one side when a shepherd and his dog slump down for a hurl along the road, and then, with a last shudder of despair, settles down to await the inevitable load of bags, boxes, plough-shanks, hay-forks, wireless batteries, and crates of chickens.

McTosh is due to leave at ten o'clock, but at eleven o'clock, he may still be seen standing by his chariot, scratching his head, and saying: " Na, I doot she'll no' haud muckle mair. Ye'll need to keep that soo back till the morn, Geordie. I'll ha'e to be windin' her up noo."

Once she gets going, there is no doubt that her presence is felt as well as heard. The passengers shake like jellies as she heaves them up and down ; chickens screech, and pigs squeal, an old wag-at-the-wa' on its way to be mended chimes with every vibration, and McTosh yells above the din : " Haud ticht. We're awa'."

With a wild plunge, the dilapidated chariot careers forward, and the perilous journey has begun. But, however willing the Baneshaker might be, there is no straight run to town for her. Cottagers, hearing the camsteerie, rush to their doors, wave to McTosh to stop, while they hand in parcels or commission him to "Get a new bottle frae the Chemist," or "Hand in ma buits to be mended," or "Ca' in at ma guid-dochter's an' tell her the coo's cauved."

McTosh accepts all orders as a matter of course, writing them down with a stub of pencil in a school jotter. Then, with a plunge at the gears, he sets the Baneshaker in motion once more, and another mile or two are covered before he stops at a wayside pillar-box.

The passengers settle down for a rest while he finds his keys, opens the box, gets out the mail, inserts the date of the next collection, and—as by this time the Baneshaker has usually given up the ghost—gets going with the starting-handle once more.

. . . .

Before the town is reached, he is in and out of the 'bus a dozen times. "I could walk it juist aboot as quick," he confesses, "but, efter a', whit's the hurry?"

Most of the passengers are out to make a day of it, and are not unduly disturbed by McTosh's dalliance. It is the live-stock who make most protest, and, indeed, there are times when pandemonium reigns inside the Baneshaker.

When at last the 'bus rattles into the main street of the town, the populace, knowing well what is coming, scurry on to the pavement, well out of reach of McTosh's erratic steering.

"Nervish craturs, thae toon's-fowk," says he, bringing his chariot to a sudden stop, perilously near a lamp-post, and jerking his passengers out of their seats. "Weel, here ye are, safe an' soond."

He has the air of having reached the North Pole, after a long and hazardous voyage, and indeed many of the passengers feel the same. As for the Baneshaker, she slumps down, lop-sided, and creaks with relief, as McTosh tackles the task of unpacking her.

"I'll be stertin' hame aboot three o'clock," he says, "or mebbee twa, if I get through ma messages in time. If no', it'll be fower."

THE VILLAGE BUS

McTosh wha runs the village bus
Aye sterts it up wi' muckle fuss
Till, roarin' like a ragin' beast
Sparks skitin' whaur expeckit least,
It gies a shoogle an' a stotter,
Mair like a monster than a motor.

McTosh syne loups intil his sate
As if the cratur' wadna wait.
"Haud ticht," he yells ; an' aff we go
Whuther we're ready or we're no',
The bus like ane demented dirlin',
An' hauf the fowk wi' anguish skirlin'.

Aye packit to its hinmaist place
It stots alang at sic a pace,
Raisin' the stoor an' duntin' sair
Till passengers in deep despair
Cling to the sides an' think they're deein' ;
But aye the bus gangs faster fleein'.

42

At stoppin'-places on the road
McTosh loots doon to lift a load
O' pokes an' parcels, e'en a soo ;
(He wadna hain to hoose a coo),
An' still the closer we maun huddle
Till beasts an' fowk are in a muddle.

But i' the end he bangs the brakes ;
The bus sits doon wi' mony shakes,
An', feelin' onything but stoot,
We coont oor wounds an' stummle oot ;
While Jehu, haein' conquered Natur',
Rewards the puffin' bus wi' waitter.

THE VILLAGE FAIR

Once a year, in peace-time, the three-cornered piece
of ground, known as *The Cockit Hat*, at the foot of the
village, is transformed from a divotty patch of waste-
ground into a colourful setting, fit for a scene from
" The Arabian Nights." Gilded chariots, somewhat
dilapidated and tawdry, drive up and spill their contents
of dark-skinned gipsies ; coco-nut shies appear as if by
magic ; Cheapjack Charlie and his wife set up their
stalls ; and soon the tinny music of the round-a-bouts
can be heard mingling with the general dirdum.

Cautious housewives take in their washing and lock
their hen-house doors ; yet before long they fall victim
to the glib, wheedling tongue of the Caravan Queen who
comes round to speir " if the leddy wi' the lucky face
could spare a sowp o' milk for the starvin' bairns ?" or
to the ragged child, " chitterin' wi' cauld," who has
been sent to beg for " onything frae a gravat to a dish-
cloot."

The village youngsters are agog with excitement. Romance has suddenly entered their midst. *The Cockit Hat* holds more glamour to them than they can find in all the story-books in the world. There are rumours of a lion in a cage, and of a monkey that turns somersaults. They stare at the piebald ponies, and gaze, entranced, into the caravans, sighing at an unkind fate, which keeps them chained to a humdrum home. Not one of them, if they had the chance, would refuse to be " off with the wraggle-taggle gypsies."

On the day of the Fair, there is little work done in the village or in the neighbouring farms. Even the Minister discards his dog-collar and forsakes his sermon, and Mrs. McWhinnie shuts up shop : " For wha wants to buy ma pandrops on a day like this ? Forbye, I'm wantin' a hurl on the roondaboots an' the shuggy-boats masel'."

Without doubt, the round-a-bouts are the greatest attraction. It is surprising how many douce folk, who would normally never dream of kicking up their heels, are now clutching the manes of painted ponies, or sprawling astride garish-looking cockerels, shrieking at the pitch of their voices, shouting and waving to their friends below, and echoing the too-loud strains of " Daisy Bell."

Dignity is forgotten. Mrs. McWhinnie's garters, which she wears well below the knee, are a kenspeckle sight before the day is out. " But, hoots ! " says she, unconcerned, " I ha'e to gi'e them an' airin' sometimes."

Above the hurly-burly can be heard the ringing of Cheapjack Charlie's bell, and his sing-song voice, inviting all and sundry to " Come forrit an' try ma amazin' bargains. I've got everything ye'll need frae the creddle to the grave ; preens, pans, cheeny, cough-mixture, combinations, whurly-gigs, jotters, buit-laces, sugaralla, gold watches, tin tacks, an' aspidistras—a' gaun at the maist reedeeculous prices . .

" Here's a fine line in men's braces ! . .

" Hand up the galluses, wife. See here, noo. It'll stretch frae here to there an' never split . .

" Lodsake ! there maun be a flaw in this ane. Hand up anither, wife. Noo, I'm no' askin' for a shillin'. I'm no' even askin' a saxpence."

Voice from the crowd, " Ye'd better no'."

" Threepence and it's yours, wi' a collar-stud thrawn in."

Mrs Charlie does her bit by roaming among the crowd, delivering goods to bidders, and collecting the money which she thrusts into a hidden " pooch " in her trailing skirt. Often, to the great delight of the onlookers, a guerilla warfare starts up between the two and Charlie's irate " asides " add much to the fun of the Fair. " If ye dinna haud your tongue, I'll gi'e ye awa' as a free sample," is his final shot.

Charlie does a roaring trade with his pills and potions, which he guarantees will cure " onything frae a sair heid to the measles—an' ye needna glower at me like that, wife. I ken they'll no' cure *your* temper."

Before long the gimcrack goods are cleared from the stall, and now repose in the pockets, and under the oxters of his customers who, once they have had leisure to examine them, begin to have doubts as to their genuineness. A disgruntled hauflin discovers that his half-crown " gold " watch is minus a hand, and Mrs. McWhinnie begins to exercise grave fears as to the efficacy of the " magic " potion, which can either be taken internally or used as furniture polish. But by now, Charlie and his wife (laden down with her " pooch") have declared a truce, and adjourned to the local inn to "wat their thrapples" and congratulate themselves on the credulity of the crowd.

The "Menagerie" is a great attraction, especially to the children, who are not critical enough to notice its flaws. It consists of a few moth-eaten monkeys, a dispirited lion, a stuffed-looking snake, which never bats an eyelid, and a "leopard" of unlikely hue. It is presided over by a worthy, who would not look amiss behind bars himself—indeed, it is more than likely that he has spent part of his life in this way. He has a manufactured foreign accent, a mahogany complexion, "Flags of all Nations" tattoed on his chest, and an evil-looking black bottle in his hip pocket. Altogether, he looks a thorough-going rascal, but to the bairns, he is one of the wonders of the world.

After refreshing himself from the bottle, he cracks his whip and shouts: "Walk hup, walk hup, and see ze most amazing collection of wild animals in ze world ; hall genuine harticles, captured by yours truly at great risk of life and limb. This snake I found on ze banks of ze River Zambesi. I fought with him for two solid hours. I was halmost exhausted, but in the hend, I mesmerised 'im, and soon he was heating out of my 'and."

Admiring chorus of : "Jings !" "Goveydick !" "Losh me !" from his fascinated audience.

Another sip from the bottle and : "It was on the banks of ze Mississippi that I met ze lion. He was hout for blood, and ready for a kill. I have ze scar to this day." He tears open his shirt, and among the "Flags of all Nations," there is indeed something that might well be a scar.

Gasps of awe from the crowd, and a yawn of sheer boredom from the lion.

" It was on the banks of ze—er—." (Another sip). " Ze—er—River Nile that I fought ze leopard. He sprang at me hout of ze jungle," . . and so on, *ad nauseam*.

If it were not for the other joys that call them—the lucky dips, the coconut shies, the hoopla, the Fat Lady, (" I think verra little o' *her*," grunts Mrs. McWhinnie, who can beat her by a stone or two any day), the " shuggy-boats," and the performing mice—the bairns would stay all day in the pungent tent, while daring deeds on the banks of the Zambesi whirl before their enamoured eyes.

Madame Tambourine (patronised by crowned heads) holds Court in a nearby caravan. She is said to be related to the lion-taming gentleman, but whether she is his wife, or his mother, or merely a capture from the Mississippi, is not known. It is thought, however, that she must have come from a warmer clime, for she has a persistent cold in the head, and does not appear to have heard of the invention of the handkerchief. Consequently, her " readings " are given to the accompaniment of violent sniffs and snorts.

Madame Tambourine works miracles. Servant girls and bondagers who mount the steps to her darkened caravan with only some small change in their shabby purses, come down again all smiles, with fortunes practically in their pockets, and promises of handsome husbands thrown in. What matter if her prognostications never come true ? For a shilling a time, she has cheered and beglamoured their humdrum lives. To-morrow they may be mucking out the byre as usual, but there is always the thought of the fortune, and the handsome man to beguile their minds, and take the tang out of the dung.

Mrs. McWhinnie refuses to enter the caravan—indeed, it would be impossible—and, for sixpence extra, Madame Tambourine graciously descends to her level, and flatters her so much that with sudden and unusual generosity, she parts with half-a-crown without a pang. " For, mexty me ! what's a hauf-croon to the likes o' me, when I'll be rollin' in wealth within a twalmonth ? "

Towards evening, the fun grows faster and more furious. The round-a-bouts whirl with greater speed, and their tinny music takes on an even more blaring note. Cheapjack Charlie sets up another stall, which resembles the Old Curiosity Shop, and his patter is now interspersed with hiccups and witticisms that set the crowd roaring with laughter. Mrs. McWhinnie—game to the end—comes a cropper in the " shuggy-boats," and consoles herself with a sip from the menagerie man's bottle, and the Minister, having won a pair of " diamond" earrings at hoopla, and winded the man at the coconut shy, takes a final turn on the round-a-bouts, and heads reluctantly home to a cold supper, and the tail-end of his sermon.

All too soon it is over. " I'll be a' the colours o' the rainbow the morn," sighs Mrs. McWhinnie, limping home with a coco-nut below one oxter, and a china dog under the other, " but, jings, it was worth it. I've used mair muscles the day than I ever kent I possessed."

Next day, *The Cockit Hat* is desolate and deserted. There is nothing to remind the villagers of yesterday's delights, except the marks of caravan wheels and a few empty coco-nut shells. The bairns are forced to return to their desks and their lessons, but their thoughts, instead of being fixed on the Battle of Bannockburn, are still whirling round with the round-a-bouts, or following the menagerie man up the Mississippi.

" Ay, it's a sair come-doon," sighs Mrs. McWhinnie, leaning desolately on her counter. " For twa preens, I'd shut up ma shop and buy a caravan—if I could get ane big enough. But, hoots, the Fair'll be back again next year. It's a' I ha'e to look forrit to—that, an' ma fortune. Did ye say a pennyworth o' black strippit bools, Mrs. McConnochie ? Eh, whowh ; this time yesterday, me an' the Meenister were on the shuggy-boats thegither . ."

THE SPAEWIFE

Ance in a while the Gypsy Queen,
Or so she ca's hersel', is seen
Slinkin' frae ane door to anither,
Leavin' the lassies in a dither
Wi' promises o' handsome men
An' faimilies as lairge as ten ;
Dodsakes ! it fairly gaurs ye grue
To think o' things that micht come true.

In tattered shawl an' shauchlin' shoon,
Her hand aye cravin' for a boon,
Wi' gab sae glib she e'en could mooch
The bawbees frae a pauper's pooch,
She'd tak' the carpet aff the flair,
An' no' content wad speir for mair.
Dootless, when at oor loofs she's keekin'
It's aye *her* fortune that she's seekin'.

But, losh ! it's worth a pickle pence
To hear ye hae sae muckle mense
To airn some day a lang degree
Or seek your fame ayont the sea ;
An', fegs ! ye'll even find her willin'
To croon ye, for an aixtra shillin'.
Sma' wunner that oor heids are bummin'
To think o' a' the luck that's comin'.

She leaves us laden-doon wi' wealth ;
An' syne we find, by cunnin' stealth
The tarry-fingered Gypsy Queen
In a' oor hen-hooses has been,
An' cleared the claes-line o' its load
Afore she hirpled doon the road ;
But, think o' a' oor future bliss !
Toots ! twa-three sheets we'll never miss.

THE GYPSY QUEEN

Nae croons hae I or gowden orbs,
Nae silks or jewels fine ;
Ma chariot's but a cuddy-cairt,
Nae gear hae I to tyne.

A humble howff ma palace is,
A caravan at whiles ;
Ma only treasure's pots an' pans
An' fortune-tellin' wiles.

An' yet ma realm is lang an' braid,
An' a' the trible is mine,

For tho' nae queenly life I lead,
I'm heid o' a' ma line.

An' aye me lichtest word is law,
An' ilka ane's ma frien'
For tho' I'm duddy, puir an' auld,
I'm still the Gypsy Queen.

CHARLIE THE CHEAPJACK

Every year, " Chairlie the Cheapjack " and his wife
turn up in our village with a cuddy-cairt packed full of
" Amazing Bargains " which range from feeding-bottles
to bicycle tyres ; or, as Chairlie puts it, " everything
ye'll need frae the creddle to the grave."

The old piebald horse who draws this wonderful
collection snorts with relief when the cuddy cairt comes
to a halt and he is set free to roll on the village green
while the goods are unloaded. Mrs. Chairlie, who is a
great giantess of a woman undertakes this task, while
her husband who is about half her size, does a propaganda tour of the village.

He begins well enough in a sing-song voice, inviting
all and sundry to " Come to the roup. Free samples
given away. Preens, pans, cheeny, cough mixture,
woollen combinations, whurleygigs, binder twine, jotters,
shoe laces, sugaralla. Everything ye'll need frae the
creddle to the grave."

Half-way through, however, his thirst always gets
the better of him, and he retires to the local inn, from
which he is rescued by his irate wife in time to start the
" proceedin's."

It is perhaps fortunate that propaganda makes Chairlie thirsty, for when the roup begins he is always in fine fettle, although a trifle unsteady on his pins. He rolls up his sleeves, thrusts an old straw basher on his head, gives a defiant glare at his wife, a grin of welcome to his customers, and launches forth into a spate of sales talk.

"Weel, here we are again, as fu' o' bargains as an egg is o' meat. Noo, let's see. Whit'll I begin wi'? Och ay, a fine line in men's braces. Hand's up the galluses, Maggie. See this, noo. It'll stretch frae here to there an' never . . Jings, there's something wrang wi' this ane. Never mind, hand's up anither ane, Maggie. Noo, I'm no askin' twa shillin's; I'm no even askin' ane shillin'. Saxpence, an' it's yours, wi' a collarstud thrown in."

Mrs. Chairlie does her bit by roaming about among the crowd like a cart-horse, delivering goods to bidders, and collecting money which she thrusts into a hidden pocket in her trailing skirt. Various clashes occur between her and her husband, but, to the great delight of the crowd, Chairlie always comes out on top, until the uplifting effects of his visit to the inn have worn off.

"Haud your tongue, Maggie," he reproves her. "It's *me* that's the Auctioneer, an' I'll gi'e awa' as mony free samples as I like. Noo, wha wants a bottle o' cough mixture? There's a man ower there hoastin' awa' like an auld coo. See here, billie, I'll let ye ha'e this bottle for fowerpence, an' if it doesna cure the cauld, it'll come in handy for furniture polish."

Chairlie welcomes back-chat from the crowd, and is undismayed by any amount of heckling, for which he has always a pawky answer. His good humour never fails, even though his voice may show signs of giving out, and he has been known in a fit of exultation to sell even the cuddy-cairt and the piebald horse, which Mrs. Chairlie has been forced to buy back to keep the concern going.

On one occasion, a jocular customer even went the length of bidding for the giantess herself, only to be told by Chairlie that he would willingly " gi'e her awa' as a free sample." Next day, however, his black eye bore witness to the fact that Maggie had tasted the fruits of revenge.

As the roup wears on, Chairlie's voice gradually gets weaker until it disappears altogether, and his wife comes into her own. *Her* voice never shows signs of weakening. She towers above the customers, terrifying them with her glare and with the fierce banging of her hammer, and, but for the antics of Chairlie behind her back, the rest of the " proceedin's " would end in dismal failure.

" See here," she will roar in a voice that could well be heard at the other end of the village. " Ye canna afford no' to buy this scrubbing brush. It'll only cost ye saxpence, and it'll save ye mair than that in elbow-grease in hauf an hoor. Come on, noo ! I'm ashamed o' ye bein' sae slow. You, mistress, ower there, ye'll tak' ane ! "

It is a command rather than a request, and the unfortunate customer is forced to bid rather than bear the brunt of Mrs. Chairlie's tongue. Chairlie, however, pours oil on troubled waters by threatening his wife with a scrubbing brush behind her back, and giving away a stick of rock with each purchase.

Maggie is, if anything, a bigger liar than her husband, She will sell, convincingly, " real gowd watches " for half-a-crown, swear that her patent pills will cure " onything frae a sair heid to the measles," insist that

her " cheeny " is unbreakable and that her special line
in jumpers came " straicht frae Paris."

Chairlie pushes his basher to the back of his head,
listens in wonderment to her flow of language, and
occasionally advises her in a husky voice to " Go to it,
Maggie ! Ye're like Hitler, the bigger the lee ye tell,
the easier it's swallowed."

At last, however, the final free sample is given away
and the roup comes to an end. Chairlie retires once
more to attend to his thirst, while his indefatigable wife
counts the money from her pockets and packs up the
the left-over goods.

Next day the piebald horse is back between the shafts
of the cuddy-cairt, and the cheapjack and his wife drive
off to their next port of call with their " Amazing
Bargains."

THE RAGMAN

When Rab the Ragman mak's his roond
Ye'll hear his auld tin-trumpet soond,
An' syne the piebald horse comes trottin',
The cuddy-cairt ahint him stottin'.

The bairns rin skelter to his side
To find what toys the cairt'll hide ;
An' wives look oot ilk dud an' duster,
An' ony rags that they can muster.

Balloons an' lucky-bags galore
Come oot frae Rabbie's endless store,
An' sune the dirdum an' the steerie
Gangs on till ilka lug is wearie.

An' "Haste ye back," we aye maun ca'
When Rabbie tak's his cairt awa' ;
An' aff he stots wi' muckle jummlin',
Oor duddy claes ahint him tummlin'.

NATURE'S LESSON

Ilk' mornin' as I gang to schule
The birdies whustle : " Sic a fule
To waste a bonnie simmer day
When ye could jouk awa' an play."

An' aft to plunk I am inclined
But aye the maister's words I mind ;
" Noo, gin ye lairn your lesson weel
Aiblins ye'll be a famous chiel."

But, och ! inside ma donnert pate
I canna haud ilk' battle's date,
For a' ma thochts are aye ootbye,
An' lairn I canna tho' I try.

But when the schule has skailed at last,
An' when the tawse's work is past,
Nae brichter loon ye'll find than me
As aff I rin to speil a tree.

Ay, lairnin' may be unco fine,
But no' for sic a heid as mine ;
Yet, tho' I'm dunce o' a' the schule,
At Nature's lairnin' I'm nae fule.

KATE THE CADGER.

Kate the Cadger has been a kenspeckle figure in our district for almost half-a-century and is still, according to her own verdict: " As yauld as a yite." As she is seldom seen out of her ramshackle van, which bears the lop-sided and misspelt inscription: " KATE McCONNOCHIE, GENERAL DEELER," it is difficult to judge her agility; but she leaves us in no doubt as to the " yauldness " of her tongue, which never stops, even when she has no other audience than McTosh, the piebald pony.

Kate sells everything from mouse-traps to mangles, with a fine range in between of clay pipes, paraffin, jotters, shoe-laces, mouth-organs, pot-plants, castor-oil, and tackety boots. Nor is she nonplussed if asked for such unlikely things as dambrods, sermon-paper, or fiddle-strings.

" Ask an' ye shall receive," is her motto; and though she has to turn her cart inside-out to do so, she usually pounces on the required goods in the end, albeit they may be faintly scented with paraffin oil or squashed almost out of recognition by the weight on top of them.

It is a mystery how McTosh stands the strain, for Kate is no mean bulk herself, and her merchandise overflows until heather brooms and milking-pails dangle out of the back, and ladles and tin cans trail over the sides, the whole setting up a dirdum which heralds her approach long before she is seen. Luckily McTosh is a well-fed, placid beast, who sets his own pace, and as often as not his own course, and will not deviate from it, no matter how Kate might cajole or reprimand him.

Because of this flight of temperament on McTosh's part and because of his mistress's thirst for clashmaclavers, there is never any regularity in Kate's visits. She is equally likely to arrive bright and early in the morning before households are stirring, or to clatter up in her equipage at ten o'clock at night. Time means nothing to Kate, although in default of a watch she carries a sizable kitchen clock in her cart; and though it can seldom be found among the conglomeration of goods, its alarum has a disturbing habit of going off at odd times throughout the day.

She takes care, however, to keep her " wee bottle " in a handy place, for she is susceptible to "turns" which can only be cured by what she calls her "physeec." There is little doubt as to its potency, for it has the effect of rousing her to such a pitch of joviality that McTosh is left to take his own airt while she regales him with selections from the Auld Scots Sangs.

In her more serious moments, Kate does her bit for the soldiers by knitting enormous "gravats" while ambling along the country roads between calls. There are times when the wool becomes entangled with mouse-traps and milk-jugs, and others when it falls out of the cart altogether and trails for miles behind her on the road; but the knitting goes on just the same, and, as Kate says: "Whit's a wheen drappit steeks amang frien's?"

Her method of doing business, as in everything else, is haphazard in the extreme. When she reaches a customer's cottage, she hitches up the reins, yells "Cadger!" and settles down for a lengthy blether with the goodwife. Occasionally, she will heave herself out of her cart and step inbye for a cup of tea, but more often she prefers to hold court in her own domain, where she declares she is: "Mair at hame than sittin' stiflin' in a hoose, an' forbye I canna lippen on McTosh to wait for me."

Usually she has to stir up the entire contents of the cart to find what her customer wants, and is apt to say, if her eye lights on another object than the one asked for : "Wad cocoa no' do ye instead o' saut ?" Or : "Hoo aboot tryin' this tooth-paste ? I canna lay ma hands on the flair-polish."

She is equally thowless in the matter of payments. Her accounts are done in a tattered jotter with the aid of a stump of pencil and a pair of steel-rimmed spectacles which she proudly declares are "Hand-'em-doons frae ma Granny." Amounts are totted up in a hit-or-miss fashion and, if ready money is being paid, it is thrust carelessly into a leather pouch, or as often as not into McTosh's nose-bag by mistake.

If the goods are on "tick," the account is entered into the jotter under a system which can be intelligible to nobody, and Kate least of all. "If only the pownie could coont," she often sighs, "I wadna care to ca' the King ma cousin."

Her call may be a short or a lengthy one, depending on McTosh's mood ; for if he suddenly decides to move off, no force on earth will stop him, and Kate often has to shout over her shoulder to a customer : "I'll gi'e ye the rest next time I ca' roond, Mistress, but juist say the word if ye're unco anxious for the scrubbin'-brush, an' I'll thraw it oot on the roadside."

On the other hand, if McTosh settles down for a long rest, there is nothing for it but to await his pleasure. Kate accepts the situation philosophically, declaring : "It gi'es me a' the mair time for a blether."

In spite of or because of her strange ways, Kate is a welcome sight as she comes jingling along the road. Children run to greet her, and the wives look forward to her pawky gossip and to rummaging in her cart where unexpected treasures often come to light. Tinkers and gaberlunzies of all descriptions are glad to encounter her on the road, and—if McTosh will deign to stop—she often does business with them, buying their entire packs and emptying the contents in beside the jumble that is already cluttering her cart.

But it is the birds and animals who are her best friends. As no man has ever " fashed her wi' his attentions," and as she declares she " wadna swap her physeec for the hale jing-bang o' them," she turns instead to lame dogs, stray cats, and wild birds, whose calls she can imitate with surprising skill. Many of them come flying round her cart, knowing that they will be fed, either from McTosh's nose-bag or from Kate's own " denner-poke," which might contain anything from a pork-pie to an apple-dumpling. Without stopping to think of her own needs, she distributes lavish helpings to her friends, consoling herself with applications to the " wee bottle " and the remark that : " It's no' lost what a frien' gets."

Often stray cats find shelter in her cart, and there is always a mongrel or two bringing up the rear. Kate talks to them as she does to McTosh, as if they were human beings, discussing such subjects as the War, the weather, and the price of coals ; and declares that " they ken mair aboot the warld and its ongauns than fowk gi'e them credit for."

When a car comes along to disturb her peaceful meanderings, Kate, far from drawing in to the side, remains firmly in the centre of the road, ignoring irate hootings, and loudly (and unnecessarily) advising McTosh to " tak' his ain time."

The situation reaches an *impasse* until a cross-roads comes in sight, or unless the car can squeeze past with wheels almost in the ditch, and Kate's brushes and pails scraping the shining surface. Many wordy battles are fought between cadger's cart and car, but it is always Kate who conquers, for there is no stemming her flow of invective, and threats of " the law " only serve to whet her appetite for further voluble onslaughts.

But, when there are no cars in sight, Kate's equipage is a decoration rather than a menace to the country roads, and her customers hope that her cheerful call of " Cadger ! " will long be heard at their cottage-doors.

BELLA, THE POSTIE.

Big Bella on her bouncin' byke
Comes aft in contact wi' a dyke
When rattlin' on her country roonds ;
An' yet, in spite o' mony wounds
She aye deleevers up the mail,
An' reads the postcairds withoot fail.

An' " Post ! " fou lood ye'll hear her roar
As, stechin' up to ilka door,
She gies the byke a michty bash
An' steps inbye to hae a clash ;
An' as wi' tea she droons her drooth
Folk's characters flee north an' sooth.

Sae fond o' havers is the cratur'
That, fegs, t'wad be against her natur'
To pass e'en gaberlunzies by
Until she's drained the birkies dry ;
As Minister o' Information
She'd be a menace to the nation.

She even blethers to the byke,
Or havers wi' a wan'erin' tyke,
An' kens far mair aboot yoursel'
Than ye could ever hope to tell;
An' though she cairries roond the papers
Dodsakes! her tongue can cut sic capers,
To read the news we needna care
For Bella tells us a'—an' mair.

THE KIRK CHOIR.

Ilk Sawbath roond the organ staund
A tuneless, tho' weel-meanin' baund,
Wha sing the psalms wi' sic a steerie
That whiles e'en Dauvid maun be wearie.

There's Muckle Wull: wi' drummlie soond
He gaurs ilk lug wi' torture stoond;
An' aye sae sweart to end the singin'
That on " Amen " ye'll hear him hingin'.

An' syne the tenor, Rabbie Broon—
A moose wad squeak a better tune.
He's aye ahint, an', wi' a haster,
He ends the vairse in sic a slaister.

There's Jess, wha skirls up to the skies—
She canna sing, but fegs, she tries;
An' o' them a' the ane that's proodest
Is Mary-Ann, wha sings the loodest.

Nae competeetion wull she thole
Frae ony ither humbler soul,
But glowers doon at the congregation
Gin they sing oot abune their station.

Aiblins the choir afore they're dune
Micht hit the same note, late or sune ;
Yet tho' they're timmer aye an' deivin',
Nae doot they'll soond a' richt in Heeven.

IT'S A QUIET LIFE IN THE CITY !

Aunt Martha, with her bandbox, came up from the country recently to pay me a visit. She feels sorry for me having to live in a top flat in the midst of a great city.

" It's that quiet ! " she declared the first morning. " I miss the cocks crawin'."

" But there are plenty of other noises," I protested, looking out of the window at a stream of 'buses, trams, and jeeps.

" Oh, that dirl ! I mean real noises, hamely things like the roadman gi'ein' me a shout in the bygaun, an' the cairter's horses clatterin' past the door. Ye're fair lost to the world up here."

Just then the mail plopped through the letter-box.

" That's the post," I remarked, going to fetch the letters.

Aunt Martha's face brightened for a moment, and then darkened as she heard footsteps retreating down the stairs.

" Is he no' comin' in ? " she asked, in a disappointed voice. " Shairly ye micht offer him a wee cup o' tea."

I explained that in the city, one did not offer the Postman " wee cups o' tea," that I did not even know his name, and had, in fact, only spoken to him once, when signing for a Registered Letter.

Aunt Martha was dumfounded. " Ye dinna ken his name, or hoo mony bairns he has, or whether he's got the rheumatics ! Mexty, you toon's-fowk ha'e a queer way o' livin'. Dodsakes, there's no' a mornin' gangs by, but what me an' Wully-the-Post has a grand blether, whether he's got any letters for me or no'. Ay, an' he often splits the kindlin' for me or cairts in a pail o' coal, an' he aye gets his drink o' tea. I'm thinkin' there's no' muckle hospitality in the toon."

She sighed and looked out of the window at the hurly-burly of the street. " A' thae fowk passin' each ither by without a frien'ly word. It's fair waesome."

There was a ring at the bell and I heard the milk-boy departing, after depositing a bottle at the door. I looked guiltily at Aunt Martha.

" That was the milkman," I confessed, " and I've no idea whether he's married or still at school. He might even have a glass eye for all I know."

Aunt Martha looked shocked, then her eye glittered reminiscently. " Big Teenie brings ma milk i' the mornin's, an' she doesna' dump it at the door in that unceevilised manner. Na, she comes in an' sits doon at the fire, and gi'es me a' the clashmaclavers o' the countryside."

" What about going out for a walk ? " I suggested, afraid lest the laundry or coalman should arrive next and Aunt Martha find me equally ignorant of their family affairs. " It's a lovely day."

"Ay," she agreed, putting on a coat, which seemed a near relative to the dolman. "I've nae doot it'll be a braw day in the country."

As we went down a woman hurried past us on the stairs, carrying a shopping-basket.

"Wha's that?" Aunt Martha wanted to know.

I avoided her gaze. "I'm not quite sure, but I—er —think she's a neighbour of mine."

"A neebour, but ye're no' shaire! Dod, that bates a'." And Aunt Martha lapsed into a silence more disconcerting than her volubility.

We walked along the crowded pavement, jostling with business-men, housewives, American sailors, Poles, and all and sundry. Aunt Martha's sharp eyes noted everything, but she sighed to think there was "no' a kent face amang them."

Her eye caught sight of a policeman on points duty. She stopped to watch him for a while.

"Puir man, he must be dyin' for a cup o' tea," she said sympathetically. "He's no unlike oor Bobby at hame, except that Rubbert hasna' got sic a fancy white coat. He must be feelin' lanely wi' naebody to speak to him. D'ye no' think I'd better gang ower an' ask him . . ?"

But I drew her away in time, and took her for a ride on top of a tramcar, which she considered "a shoogly contraption that fairly dunts up your internals."

At the end of another day, Aunt Martha packed up her bandbox. "I canna thole the quiet ony langer," she confessed. "I'm dyin' to get hame to hear a' the clashes."

Her eye brightened as she gazed unseeingly out of the window, at the stirring ant-heap of humanity below. "I wadna' wunner but Big Teenie's coo'll ha'e cauved. Ay, there's aye something happenin' in the country.

CITY SPEUG.

When ither stervin' sangsters flee
To warmer shores ayont the sea,
When squirrels sleep an' kye gang eild,
Ye never seek a better beild.

Sair trauchled aye to find your fare,
Ilk' crumb o' comfort I can spare
Ye gobble doon wi' gratefu' speed,
Shakin' the hailstanes frae your heid.

Aiblins ye ken when things gang wrang
I lippen on your wunter sang ;
Sic smeddum in a beast sae sma'
Can teach a lesson to us a'.

THE PLUNKER.

Ahint the drystane dyke he jouks
An' keeks abune wi' stealthy looks ;
Ayont the burn, wi' dirlin' clang
The schule-bells sing a noisy sang.

But no' for him the desk an' slate,
Wi' lessons he'll ne'er fash his pate ;
The burn is his the hale lang day,
He'll guddle troots, whate'er they say.

An' sae while ithers rack their brains
An' lairn o' Kings—wi' muckle pains—
As free as ilka bird that flees
He lauchs at rules, an' tak's his ease.

But when the mirk fa's doon at nicht
The callant's feelin' no' sae bricht,
For tho' the day he's lauched at laws,
The morn he maun face the tawse !

THE TRAVELLING GEGGIE

In the days of the penny geggie, when entertainments
were crude, but hearty, a " family company " toured
the countryside giving performances in every village,
to the great delight of the uncritical audiences, who
welcomed them wherever they went. At the head of
the troupe was a big, jovial man, known as Tourin' Tam,
who had one wooden leg and an endless thirst, neither
of which disabilities hindered his prowess in the
dramatic arts.

The rest of the cast consisted of Mrs. Tam, his leading
lady, who shared his thirst, and a large family of children
who nobly took any part from Little Nell to Dirty Dick.
There were also two performing dogs, and a piebald
pony which drew their " cuddy-cairt," and appeared on
the stage when the occasion arose.

It was a miracle how the company, their effects and
their household pots and pans, all contrived to fit into
the " cuddy-cairt," and how the piebald pony managed
to draw such a burden. But as Tourin' Tam was never

in a hurry, and as he had no " first nights " arranged, they ambled round the countryside at their own pace, jangling and rattling at every step. A battered bill was pasted on the back of the equipage to the effect that this was " Tourin' Tam and his Company. Drama at its Biggest and Best." In humbler letters, it stated : " Pots and Pans Mended. Heather Brooms for Sale."

When the colourful procession arrived at the outskirts of a village, the company unravelled themselves and prepared for action. If a Bellman was in the district, he was sent round to inform the people that : " A stupendous attraction has arrived. Tourin' Tam an' his Troupe will gi'e a performance doon in the haugh, where a hair-raising drama will be acted." Sometimes, Tourin' Tam acted as Bellman himself, ringing his bell vigorously, and giving dramatic excerpts from his plays in the village street.

Seldom, however, did he get past the local Inn, from which his irate leading lady had to rescue him in time to help with the props.

Meanwhile, the children were sent from door to door, begging chairs for the " theatre," and old clothes for the players, at the same time doing a trade in heather brooms, and inquiring if there were any pots and pans to mend. Then they all congregated at the place chosen for the performance, and set to work to erect their rough-and-ready theatre.

If the weather was fine, the performance took place in the open, with only a rude trestle stage for the players, and an unsteady screen to act as dressing-room. If wet, a tattered tent was brought into service, through which the rain dripped on the audience, whom Drama made immune from such petty disturbances.

Tourin' Tam, dressed in an ancient kilt, with his

wooden leg very much in evidence, stood outside the arena, and invited the populace to " Walk in, an' ha'e the treat o' your lives." The villagers were not slow to accept his invitation, for entertainments were few and far between, and Tourin' Tam's personality made him a popular figure wherever he went.

Meantime, the youngest member of the company walked among the audience, selling halfpenny pokes of pea-nuts, and answering inquiries as to the nature of the piece that was to be played. Tourin' Tam retired to his dressing-room, from which he could hear impatient shouts of, " Up wi' the Curtain." And then, as a prelude, the band (four or five of Tourin' Tam's children with tin whistles and mouth-organs) would launch forth into a ragged overture. The star in his dressing-room took one more swig from the bottle and stuck on his whiskers. The show was about to begin.

The " Dramatic Sketches " performed were usually the work of Tourin' Tam himself, aided occasionally by such lesser lights as Shakespeare, Dickens, or Scott. There was, usually, at least one murder, and Mrs. Tam could always be seen at some part of the performance ineffectually trying to conceal a large bottle of red ink. It was their most expensive item ; in a year they poured gallons of it on the shrine of Drama.

During the show there were many minor disturbances. Inquisitive cows poked their heads among the audience, the piebald pony cropped noisily round the stage, a few dog-fights livened up the proceedings, and sometimes a sudden deluge of rain ended the performance altogether, till audience and actors between them erected the tent.

Both Tourin' Tam and his leading lady put heart and soul into their acting, the rest of the cast, unfortunately, needing prompting so often that their father had to say most of their parts as well as his own. Mrs. Tam's only drawback was her deafness, which occasioned the hero to shout in her ear, so that she would pick up her cue. The audience, however, had no fault to find with actors or acting. They entered heart and soul into the spirit of the play, and occasionally were so carried away that they shouted spontaneous interpolations to the stage. " Dinna trust him, Maria ! Boo ! Dirty Scoundrel ! Look oot ! He's gaun to kill ye ! "

In between plays, there were selections from the band, " turns " by the performing dogs and the piebald pony, if it could be induced to leave the grass. Any of the children who were not taking part in the next play, danced on the unsteady stage. And so the show went on.

Tourin' Tam's greatest problem was how to get the audience to leave. They were out to make a night of it, and were determined to get their money's worth. Even after the tin whistles and mouth-organs had vigorously played " God Save The King " and " Auld Lang Syne " they lingered and would not leave till Tourin' Tam had given them " The Deid Man's Drap " at least half-a-dozen times.

This spectacular item, at which Tourin' Tam was an expert, never failed to thrill the audience. The actor would stand rigid at the front of the stage, and then, amid gasps of horror from the audience, would gradually drop flat on his back like a dead man. No matter how often Tourin' Tam yielded to his thirst, he could always be relied on to go through this sinister performance in a manner that made his audience shudder with fascinated delight.

THE DROVE ROAD

In days gane by, the auld drove road
Saw mony a steerin' sicht,
When herds an' cairts an' caravans
Went by frae morn till nicht.

An' droves o' sheep were driven there,
An' wives to merket hied,
An' packmen cairted by their wares,
An' there the peeweep cried.

An' mony a coortin' couple walked
At nicht alang its track,
An' mony a troth was plighted there
Afore they daun'ered back.

But noo the highroad tak's the steer
An' caurs birl by like stoor,
An' mossy grows the auld drove road,
Deserted hoor by hoor.

But still the peeweep hovers there,
An' still the lovers walk—
Nae modern highroad's built for love
Or canty, coortin' talk.

THE COUNTRY TRAIN

The muckle train frae London comes birlin' fu' o' pride,
Wi' cushioned sates, an' curtains, an' gentry-fowk inside ;

But aye I lo'e the little train that daun'ers here an' there,
Wi' stoorie sates, an' wunddas cracked, an' plenty time
    to spare.

There's mony a stechin' roar an' grunt afore the wheels
    gang roon',
An' when the whustle gies a blast, for miles ye'll hear
    the soon';
At ilka level-crossin' it'll stop afore the gate;
It doesna maitter muckle gin it's hauf an hoor ower late.

An' keekin' frae the wunddas we hae time to tak' a look
At hoo the hairst is gettin' on, an' even coont ilk stook;
We can wave to fowk we ken as we gang warstlin' doon
    the track,
Aiblins we micht hae time to lean oor heids oot for a
    crack.

When ilka station comes in sicht, the train'll hain its
    braith.
The station-maister roars an' rants as though he's worked
    to daith;
He'll oxter in the hirplin' wives wi' baskets, gaun to shop,
An' pick their auld umbrellas up, an' a' the things they
    drop.

What though the muckle London train a hunner mile
    may birl?
E'en though it cairries kings an' queens, an' faster still
    may whirl,
Gie me the little country train that daun'ers here an' there,
Wi' plain an' pawky fowk inside, an' plenty time to spare.

Mrs. McWhirter is terrified to be left alone with the telephone. "What'll I do if it rings?" she asks fearfully, gazing at it as if it were a wild beast that might jump on her at any moment.

"Oh, just answer it, and write down the messages on the pad," I told her airily.

"Dodsakes, if it was only as simple as that," glooms Mrs. McWhirter. "I'll keep oot its road in the kitchen, an' mebbe I'll no' hear it."

But, sure enough, the telephone waits—according to Mrs. McWhirter—until she has been forced to go near it, and then gives a shrill peal, which "fair gaurs me loup oot ma skin." Thereafter, strange pantomimes take place between Mrs. McWhirter and the instrument, the results of which I find scribbled down on the pad when I return.

There are messages from such unlikely creatures as the "Sanitary Inspector." "He had a terrible bad cauld, an' seemed awfu' anxious aboot your drains," says Mrs. McWhirter, when enlarging on the message next day. "I tell't him to rub his chest wi' embarkation, but he didna seem to ken what I was talkin' aboot. It's that tellyphone. It knocks everybody steepid."

The "Sanitary Inspector," I find, is really my cousin, ringing up about trains, and not drains.

Mrs. McWhirter declares that she would sooner "jump heid-first into the Clyde" than use the telephone herself. Therefore, I was considerably startled one morning when I lifted the receiver, and heard her exasperated voice, saying: "Hoots, haud your tongue, wumman. I ken fine I've got to press the button." Then, in a voice that would wake the dead: "Is that you? Weel, this is me."

As if repeating a lesson, she gabbled: " I have rang up to tell you that I can't come to-day."

" Goodness, what's the matter ? " I inquired, but Mrs. McWhirter, having said her say, dumped down the receiver, and vanished into the air.

Next morning, she appeared looking as if tremendous events had taken place, and announced that her " man's mother had took a stroke." But that was nothing, compared with her main theme, which might be entitled : " Ma tussle wi' the Tellyphone."

" I gaed into ane o' thae booths," she began, determined to go over every detail. " At least, I tried to get in, but it was an awfu' ticht squeeze. Ye see, I'd come oot wantin' ma specs, an' I never noticed there was a wee nyaff o' a cratur' in there already, until he let oot an awfu' yell when I stramped on his taes. Losh, his language was something chronic—an' doon the tellyphone tae !

" A'weel, I had to gang ootside an' wait till he was through, an', jings, he micht ha'e been tellin' the story o' his life—no' that it wad be muckle worth the hearin' by the looks o' him—frae the time he took.

" When he did come oot, I gied him a freezin' glower, an' says I, in ma Sunday voice : ' Are you quite sure you haven't missed onything out ? You wouldn't like for to go back, and tell them aboot Snow White and the Seven Dwarfs, would you ? ' Fegs, he fair shrivelled up, an' was roond the corner, an' oot o' sicht afore I'd got settled in the wee box.

" A'weel, it took me the best pairt o' half an hoor to read the directions, an' at the hinnerend—wad ye believe it ?—I found that I'd naethin' in ma pooch, but a three-penny bit. Dod, but it was aggravatin'.

"There were nae shops near-hand, so the best I could do was approach a puir shauchlin' kind o' man, wha was sittin' slaisterin' awa' at some pictur's on the pavement. Mercy, I could ha'e made a better job masel' wi' ma een shut.

"He was geyan taen aback when I handed him ma threepenny bit, an' asked for tippence change, an', of coorse, he gied me fower half-pennies—it was a' he had—an' I was nae better aff than before."

"What on earth did you do next, Mrs. McWhirter?" I asked, as she paused for effect.

"Weel, ma Granny used to say that the back's aye made for the burden, so there was naethin' for't but to hing aboot until the man had collected some mair coppers, an' then I did a swap wi' him. But, by the time I won back to the box, there was a queue waitin' as lang as for fish, so I juist had to stand on ane leg an' then the t'ither till it cam' to ma turn.

"I got haud o' the wifey at the ither end a' richt, but she wasna on for listenin' to me. In fact, she was that thrang tellin' somebody else that ' As shaire as daith, I seen them priced at hauf a croon,' that I micht ha'e been standin' there yet if I hadna gied a hoast that fair gaured the tellyphone trimmle, an', says I: 'If it's not too much trouble, could ye please attend to the coonter?'

"She gied a yawn, as far as I could guess, an' says she, awfu' fed up like: 'What's your number?' So I gied it to her, an' the next thing I heard was a buzzin' like a lot o' bumbees, an' then: 'Press Button A,' an' efter that an awfu' unceevil man sayin': 'Weel, what are ye wantin'?' terrible coorse like.

"'Wha micht you be?' says I. An' says he: 'I micht be Mussolini, or the King o' the Cannibal Islands,

74

but I'm no' ; I happen to be the Polis. What is't ye're wantin' ? '

" ' No' you, onywey,' says I, an' slammed doon the receiver. Noo, wasn't it aggravatin' ? I'm shaire the wifey had gied me the wrang number on purpose. An' the warst o't was, I had lost ma pennies."

" What on earth did you do next ? "

" Och, I juist pressed Button B."

" And did anything happen ? "

" Ay, twa pennies an' a back stud rummlet oot. I was rale weel pleased to see the back stud, for ma man's aye losin' his. I managed to get the richt number efter a terrible oncairry. But never again ! I'd raither put in ten hoors at the steamie ony day."

Just then the telephone gave a sharp ring, and Mrs. McWhirter fled towards the kitchen, muttering : " Dodsakes, there's nae gettin' awa' frae that fiend. If I could find the man wha invented it, I'd shut him up in ane o' his wee boxes, an' chairge a penny a shot, so I wad ! "

THE SODGER'S LAMENT

Ma Auntie's keen to do her bit ;
She knits me socks that winna fit,
An' scarves that stretch frae here to there
An' gaur me scart until I'm sair.

She sends me parcels, broad an' stoot,
Wi' hauf the contents hingin' oot ;
There's soda scones, sae hard an' dry
They'd kill the teuchest German spy.

She aye pits in some taffy knots ;
They stick in a' the queerest spots,
An' juist to mak' it past a' hope
The hale thing stinks o' scented soap.

Oh, Auntie, for your country's sake,
Forget aboot me when ye bake ;
Gin ye wad do your bit for me,
Adopt a wee evacuee.

QUEUE

Here, keep your elbows to yoursel'
An' dinna shove . . I canna tell.
I think it's fish.   It micht be eggs.
Wha's basket's duntin' on ma legs ?
I should be washin' doon the stair
But, hoots, I've plenty time to spare.
Wha's that in front ? It's Mrs. Scott.
Lodsakes !   *she's* shaire to lift the lot.
An' sic a hat !   Is that the rain ?
Here, you ahint, haud back your wean.
Thae shops are gettin' drunk wi' pooer ;
They've closed noo for the denner-hoor !
The fish's dune—that's naethin' new,
But, fegs, wha could resist a queue !

" JERRY " DIDN'T COME

Our village, " somewhere in Scotland," had its first
Air Raid Warning the other night. For months we had
been waiting anxiously for this moment, disappointed
indeed that the enemy had not thought fit to visit us
sooner. After all, we had spent many long hours in
preparation for an event that never seemed to be going
to happen.

Even Weelum, the Warden, had begun to lose the
zeal that had kept him proudly parading the darkened
street night after night.

After many a wordy battle, he had coaxed and threat-
ened the villagers into blacking out their windows, until
not even the proverbial " chink " could be seen. He
had, with more enthusiasm than knowledge, conducted
lectures in the village hall, on subjects ranging from
compound fractures to high explosives. He had given
a demonstration with our only stirrup-pump, drooking
most of the population in the process, and had completely
bamboozled us on the subject of " When, how, and
where to wear your gas mask."

All this, however, brought no results. The enemy
simply would not recognise our existence.

" I canna understand them," grumbled Weelum.
" It's no' as if we had nae military objectives. There's
the best fermin' grund i' the country roond aboot here,
forbye Tod Tamson's prize bulls i' the fields. An' then,
there's the cottage hospital. Ye'd think they wad want
a shot at that."

* * * *

But neither prize bulls nor hospitals seemed to hold
any lure for the enemy. Weelum grew discouraged.

His night patrolling became more perfunctory. Instead he began to spend his evenings with his cronies, as he had done in pre-war days, in Saunders's smiddy.

They were all there, smoking, swapping clashma-clavers, and playing draughts the other night when the warning went. As we have no sirens in our village, and as the method of raising the alarm has been debated so often, and chopped and changed from whistles to bells (and even, at one time, to a rousing dirl on the bag-pipes), it was somewhat difficult to know how to warn the people that their great moment had come at last.

Mary Ann, who keeps the local Post Office, and has the only telephone in the place, was the first to be informed by Headquarters that "enemy 'planes were approaching," and that an alert was to be sounded. As Mary Ann has not been on speaking terms with our Warden since the night when her chimney went on fire, and he accused her of belonging to the Fifth Column, she was in no hurry to pass on the information, excited though she was at the honour that had come to the village.

.   .   .   .

Weelum was huddled thoughtfully over the dambrod when she pushed open the smiddy door, and casually informed him that "The warnin's went. Ye'd better soond the alarm."

"Guid Gosh!" Weelum sprang to his feet, quivering with excitement. "An' me withoot ma tin hat an' ma uniform. I maun run hame for them at ance. An' whaur the de'il's ma bell?"

"It was a whustle ye were to blaw. The bell was for the ' All Clear.' "

78

" Awa'," cried Saunders, " It was the bell."

" Na, it was the whustle."

" I tell ye it was the bell."

" Haud your tongues," ordered Weelum. " Awa' hame an' put on your gas-masks. I'll hurry into ma uniform an' soond the alarm. Mind an' coont hoo mony bombs they drap."

When Weelum at last dashed out of his house, fully equipped in his uniform, tin hat, and gas-mask, and lugging an enormous bell in his hand, he was confronted in the street by Mary Ann.

" Ye needna' fash yersel' to ring the bell," she informed him. " Ye're ower late. The 'All Clear's' went."

" Dang it ! " cried Weelum, tearing off his gas-mask, and almost weeping with disappointment. " Could they no' ha'e waited a bit langer ? It wasna' worth their while comin'. They micht at least ha'e drappit a bomb."

And so our first Air Raid turned out to be a fiasco. But we are hoping that the Germans will be more considerate when next they visit us. After all, as Weelum says: " We're no' doin' a' this A.R.P. juist for fun."

HAME ON LEAVE

Anither step or twa an' then
I'll hae a glimpse o' oor hoose-en'
Ayont the field ;
Wi' twa-three roses on the wa'
Sheltered frae a' the wunds that blaw,
A canty beild.

I see the hairst's been unco fine
Tho' wrocht by ither hands than mine,
But, hoots, I'll stook.
An' there's the hoose, sae trig an' fit.
Guidsakes ! the parlour fire is lit.
Losh, wad ye look !

An' doon the road rins barkin' Ben.
He'd ken me 'mang a score o' men,
Or 'deed a hunner ;
An' is that mither at the yett,
The bakin' dune, the table set ?
I wadna wunner !

I'll sune forget ma fechtin' ploys
When ance I'm in ma corduroys.
Ben's still the same !
Anither yaird, an' then I'm there ;
Aff wi' ma pack an' ilka care.
Mither, I'm hame !

PEBBLE KAIL

Aunt Elspeth, in her country cottage, often has
visitors of the gaberlunzie clan, but there was something
different about the vagrant who chapped at her door
the other day. He was as ragged and down-at-heel as
the rest, but he raised his shabby hat politely, and said :
" Guidday to ye, leddy. Wad ye be doin' me a favour ? "

" It depends," said Aunt Elspeth, cautiously. " What
is it ? "

" Could ye lend me a pan for a wee while ? " he asked, and held out his hand, in which lay a small round pebble. " I haven't tasted a bite since yesterday, an' I want to mak' some pebble kail."

" Pebble kail ! " said Aunt Elspeth, " What on earth is that ? "

" Lend me a pan an' I'll let you see," he offered.

Aunt Elspeth looked doubtful, but her interest was roused, so she hurried into the kitchen in search of a pan. When she came back with it, the tramp was loud with his thanks.

" If ye could let me come in for a meenit to ha'e the use o' your fire, I'd be very gratefu'," he added humbly.

Aunt Elspeth, anxious to see the results of his cooking, consented, and once inside, her strange visitor's next request was for water. After filling the pan, and placing it on the fire, he inserted the pebble with great care, and asked for a ladle.

Aunt Elspeth watched him, fascinated. " A wee drap o' saut an' pepper wad gi'e it a flavour, if ye could spare it," he begged. His bewildered hostess obliged him, and again he thanked her profusely.

For a time he stirred vigorously. " Ye dinna happen to ha'e a pinch o' flour to stiffen the kail ? " he asked. Aunt Elspeth produced the flour and in it went.

After a few more stirs : " Ye'll no ha'e a carrot ye dinna want ? " Aunt Elspeth had. The man borrowed a knife and cut up the carrot, after which it joined the pebble in the pot.

" That's better," said he, peering in at the mixture, " but a turnip wadna come amiss." Aunt Elspeth obligingly produced a turnip, and it, too, found its way into the pot.

After more energetic stirrings, he ladled out a spoonful of broth and sampled it. "Ay," said he, smacking his lips, "it's doin' fine. There's naethin' to bate pebble kail, though it wad be nane the waur o' a tasty bit o' beef bane."

Having already gone so far, Aunt Elspeth took the hint and went further. She searched in the larder and found a bone, which the tramp accepted gratefully, and inserted into the steaming kail pot.

He smiled with satisfaction. "Jings, that's grand. It'll be ready in a jiffy. If ye can juist lend me a plate an' spune, an' spare me a hunk o' breid, that's a' I want. Ay, there's naethin' like pebble kail."

But Aunt Elspeth was at last beginning to see through his ruse. "Look here !" she said, "this pebble kail is all very well, but it would be nothing without all the tasty things I've given you. Anybody could make good broth like that, without bothering with a pebble and calling it fancy names."

"Weel, *I* couldna'," admitted the tramp, pouring out a liberal supply, and beginning to sup it with relish. "That pebble's worth a mint o' siller to me. It brings me in a tasty meal every day. Ay," he ended with a wise smile, "there's naethin' to bate pebble kail."

HAME THOCHTS

Amid the rummle o' the guns,
E'en when I'm blatt'rin' at the Huns,
I think o' hame.
Is mither at the milkin' noo ?
Does Mary Ann, oor sonsie coo,
Still stech the same ?

I wunner hoo the 'neeps hae set,
An' if the soo has littered yet ?
(Jings ! that was near).
I hope auld Tweed's aye keepin' weel ;
Hech, hoo I'd like him at ma heel
Gey faur frae here.

Whisht ! there's a mavis whustlin' clear
Abune the dirdum an' the steer ;
Its sang's the same
I've aften heard aboot oor brae ;
It gies me hope that, come what may,
I'll wun back hame.

THE WORSHIPPER

Kirkwards wi' solemn step he treads,
Nor looks to left or richt ;
The Buik ablow his oxter pressed—
A douce an' godly sicht.

An' tho' his cronies he may meet,
Nae pawky jokes he mak's ;
On Sabbath he wad ne'er indulge
In sic unseemly cracks.

The bells ring oot their solemn call,
The elders guard the plate,
As aff he doffs his Sabbath hat
An' daun'ers to his sate.

A kerchief clean comes oot his pooch,
His specs he pits in place,
Then boos his heid an' gies a prayer
To ask the Lord for grace.

An' then the Psalms he lo'es sae weel,
Wi' lusty soon' doth raise ;
An' tho' his timmer voice be cracked
The Lord accepts his praise.

" INSIDE " INFORMATION

Old Mrs. Macnab has enjoyed bad health ever since
the day she received a present from a misguided friend
of a volume, entitled, " Till the Doctor Comes." She
has gloated over the illustrations, felt all the symptoms,
and sampled all the diseases, and by now has amassed
an amazing collection of medicine bottles, from which
she takes spoonfuls between, during, and after meals,
as well as a " sowp " or two when going to bed.

The book is battered and tattered by now, but Mrs.
Macnab remains as stout and hearty as ever. Doubtless,
if she had not her " ailments " to keep her going, she
would have died long ago through sheer boredom.

Her one regret is that, so far, she has failed to achieve
an operation, but, she says hopefully: " Conseederin' the
state o' ma stammock, there's nae kennin' when I micht
need ane."

Although she declares that she " never eats a bite,"
she buys liberally from the grocer and butcher, and needs
little encouragement to toy with a third helping at a
neighbour's table.

"But," she adds, with a pained look on her healthy face, "I'll fairly suffer for't the nicht. I'm no' ane to complain, but I ken fine I'll never close an e'e. Eh! whowh! It's an awfu' thing to be afflicted wi' a stammock."

There are other parts of Mrs. Macnab's anatomy, which, from time to time, "gi'e her murder." And, when she can think of nothing more exciting she suffers from a peculiar complaint which she terms "the droops."

Sometimes this disease affects her leg (coinciding with requests from neighbours to give them a hand with the cleaning); sometimes it attacks her "inwardly." At all times it can be relied upon as a good stand-by, and though it is not actually listed in her bedside book, Mrs. Macnab has received great comfort and consolation from it.

She considers it unfortunate that the country Doctor does not understand her case, but excuses him on the plea that she has "ower mony complications for a plain man like him." Harley Street is her idea of heaven, and she breathes the word "Specialist" with awe and pride.

Somewhere, she is convinced, there is a very special "Specialist" who would give his soul to make a case of her, and if ever she comes into a legacy, she means to go to London and seek him out.

Until that day, she has to be content with the ministrations of the local Doctor, who has rushed so often to her death-bed in the small hours of the night (only to find her as large as life, gloating over her bedside book and surreptitiously quaffing a mugful of cocoa) that he would willingly send her to Harley Street or anywhere else, if only he could get rid of her.

As it is, he can only console himself by telling her heartily, whenever they meet: " You're looking blooming Mrs. Macnab. I never saw anyone in such perfect health." At which, she shakes her head over his ignorance, telling him that appearances are deceptive, and that " ma inside tells a different story."

So obsessed is she by her inside that she has long pestered him for a " photy " of it. At length, after a pretence of obliging her, he presented her with a dim and dingy print, which might have been a blurred picture of the Suez Canal, or a foggy night in London, but which certainly had nothing to do with Mrs. Macnab's inside.

It satisfied that lady, however, and she now gives it prominent place on the mantelpiece beside her china dogs, and proudly points it out to all visitors.

When she is suffering from " the droops," or from one of her more complicated diseases, she can mark the exact spot on the photograph.

" Isn't it terrible," she says, with a long-suffering sigh, " what I've had to gang through ! Ay ! when I see ma stammock sittin' there on the mantelpiece, I wonder to masel' that I'm leevin'. But," she adds, cheering up, " I've nae doot they'll be forced to operate afore lang ! "

SATURDAY PENNY

To Taffy Tam's I used to flee
Ilk' Setterday wi' muckle glee
To eye the wunners i' his wundy
An' syne stot in to buy some gundy,

Or whiles a lucky-bag I'd try,
Or sticky sugar-alla buy ;
Aiblins a taffy-aipple sweet,
Or strippit ba's, sae guid to eat.
But noo nae sweeties I can mooch.
Ma money's idle i' ma pooch,
An' sae, to stem ma mither's ravin's
I pit the penny in ma savin's.
I ken it's for ma country's sake,
To help a battleship to make ;
But, och ! a callant canna sook
The pages o' a savin's book.

SABBATH SCHULE

I hope that God'll no' be vexed
But, jings, I've clean forgot ma text,
An' whaur's ma penny for the plate ?
It's lost again, as shaire as fate.

Ma pooch is fou' o' ither things.
There's caunle ends an' bits o' strings,
But no' a penny to be seen.
Losh, fancy, here's a safety-preen.

What was the text ? Dod ! I forget.
Ma Granny wad be sair upset.
She tried to ca' it in ma heid ;
I wush that *she* could come insteed.

But there's the bell : I maunna shirk,
For God Himsel' is i' the kirk.
Jings, here's the penny in ma shoe,
An'—" Trust in Him "—I mind it noo !

THE DOCKSIDE SMIDDY.

The dockside smiddy, unlike the village smithy, is presided over by a dwarf of a man, ironically known in the district as Big Wullie. He has, however, a powerful pair of arms and a set of muscles which he is fond of displaying to customers who come in to have barrows mended, cars repaired, horses shod, or even life-boats patched up.

Nothing is too big or too small for the smith to tackle. He will undertake with equal equanimity to mend a mousetrap or a roadster, and has even been known to patch up local quarrels to the satisfaction of all parties.

His second-in-command is Little Wullie, his son, who is as big and brawny as his father is small and wizened. The rest of the staff consists of an " odd man " known as Bellows because of a perpetual wheeze in his chest. Bellows, according to the public, can always be heard before he is seen, and when he speaks (which he does with great difficulty) he has, as they say, " twa wheezes to ilka word."

The smiddy resembles a junk shop at its very worst. There is seldom a clear space on the floor, and Big Wullie is often lost behind a pile of spare parts, over which he has to clamber before he can present himself to a customer.

In the middle there is the blazing forge, and around it lie broken perambulators, old shafts, wheels, rudders, motor engines, and various undistinguishable bits of wreckage. Big Wullie, however, knows the origin of each and all of them and carries in his head a perpetual inventory of all the jobs he has done.

At the back of the smiddy, Big Wullie has cleared and

boarded off a minute space, which he proudly terms
"the Office." As neither of his assistants can stand
upright or turn round in it, no one goes near it except
Big Wullie himself. Unfortunately, it is here that he
keeps his telephone, so the perilous trail has to be
negotiated at intervals through the day.

The smiddy, with its blazing forge has, naturally, a
great attraction for the local children, who congregate
at the door and watch with fascinated eyes while the
three men ply their trade.

Big Wullie, who has a sharp tongue, professes to be
very fierce when he sees them, but there is a twinkle in
his eyes that belies his sharp words. The children know
that if they stand long enough he will leave the forge,
clamber to the office, and return with a poke of sweeties.

Meal time at the smiddy is a simple affair. Big Wullie
heats tinnies of tea at the forge, while Bellows is sent off
for hot pies. The meal is usually shared by stray cats,
for which Bellows has a passion. He takes charge of
every one he meets in the street, and often has as many
as a dozen sitting solemnly round the forge.

Hurt paws are attended to by Big Wullie as a matter
of course. "Beasts or machinery, it's a' the same to
me," says the smith.

Bellows, who adores his master, approves of everything he does, and wheezes behind him wherever he
goes. He has no life apart from the smiddy. At night
he sleeps in a shake-down in a dim corner, with the cats
for company.

Little Wullie, on the other hand, is dour and silent.
The smith, who treats him as though he were still a
child, is annoyed when he occasionally sneaks off to
the pictures. "There's that callant plunkin' again," he
complains to Bellows.

When it comes to the making up of bills and settling of accounts, the smith and his assistants are completely at sea. None of them are " guid wi' the pen," and Big Wullie puts in many painful hours in the office, scratching away at sheets of paper and coming to no definite conclusions.

Although he can keep a tally in his head of all the spare parts that are lying about, his money affairs are in a worse state of confusion than the smiddy. Often he says : " I dinna ken whether I'm a rich man or a puir ane ; but as lang as I can keep ma forge blazin' I'm no carin'."

Occasionally, Bellows receives wages, but is in no way dismayed if he doesn't.

He has no recollection of what he does with the money. Sometimes he hides it about the smiddy. Sometimes he lapses, and has a jovial night at the " local," but, usually, his only extravagance is cough drops, which he sucks non-stop in a vain endeavour to cure his wheeze.

The smiddy is a home-from-home for the Lascars, who often come in to converse with Big Wullie by means of smiles, nods, and occasional words. On cold days they enjoy the comfort of the glowing forge, and are always welcome to heat up their concoctions of food or tins of tea, or even to share a meal with the stray cats.

" We're a' Jock Tamson's bairns," the smith tells them, to which they reply with gleaming smiles and nods of their turbaned heads.

Often they bring strange presents for Big Wullie, which he stacks up in a corner of the crowded smiddy. " It gets mair like the Auld Curiosity Shop ilka day," he says, gazing fondly round his domain, and is very indignant if anyone suggests that he should tidy it up.

" Tidy ! " he snorts, " Whit for should I tidy it up ?
I'd never find onything."

And so the smiddy flourishes in cheerful confusion,
and passers-by who see the sparks flying up from the forge
go on their way with the comforting feeling that as
long as Big Wullie is there all is well with the dockside.

THE ROUP

When Lucky Broon retired frae life
(She was a crabbit, girnin' wife),
She left a hoose mair like a midden,
An' sae a public roup was bidden.

The unctioneer, auld Squeakin' Jock
(His voice wad shame a crawin' cock),
Cam' doon wi' verra sma' persuasion
To be in chairge o' the occasion.

The fowk cam' croodin', faur an' near,
To mak' a bid, an' jine the steer ;
An' as auld Jock his hammer birled,
" How muckle for this clock ? " he skirled.

The auld wife's treasures cam' to licht,
An', fegs, they were a sorry sicht ;
But aye the unctioneer wad praise them,
As high abune his heid he'd raise them.

The doctor bocht a cheeny dug
(It had a'e leg an' hauf a lug) ;
The meenister, in richt guid fettle,
Paid saxpence for a kitchen kettle.

Jock's voice rose higher wi' the bids
(He sell't for tippence twa pan-lids) ;
An' Lucky's sofa, auld an' duddy,
A tinker bocht to feed his cuddy.

But when the hoose was toom at last,
An' a' the steer an' strushie past,
Wi' oxters fu' we had to grapple—
An' Jock went aff to wat his thrapple.

COAL-CAIRT.

Puir patient beast ; ye're aye in chains,
Wi' somebody pu'in' at the reins,
Atween the shafts o' some auld cairt ;
Wi' freedom ye've had lang to pairt.

Altho' wi' blinkers on your e'e
There's mony awesome sichts ye see,
An' soonds a horse should never hear
That gaur ye stoond at times wi' fear.

Ye hing aboot frae door to door
While Tam gies oot his fearsome roar ;
It's " Coals ! " frae airly until late,
An' a' that ye can do is wait.

But, oh ! your hairt is faur awa' ;
Ayont the toon, when ye were sma'
There was a field, baith green an' sweet
Whaur ye could lie aboot an' eat.

Keep it in mind, an' dinna fret.
Ye'll gang whaur gress is greener yet ;
For aye abune the cry o' " Coals ! "
I'm shaire e'en horses hae their goals.

THE ELDER.

His wrinkled face transformed wi' pride,
He cairries roon' the plate,
An' glowers at ilka worshipper
Wha fidgets i' his sate.

An' ne'er a haund maun miss its turn
Or pass the offerin' by ;
To dodge the plate when he's in chairge
A body maun be fly.

An' when a bawbee's droppit in
Richt wrathfu' is his froon ;
But aye he gies a thankfu' nod
When saxpence rattles doon.

An' when the Laird is i' the kirk
Nae prooder man than he,
For then amang the humbler coins
A paper note he'll see.

An' then he bows fu' grand an' low,
An' wi' a pridefu' smirk,
He swaggers onward wi' the plate—
A pillar o' the kirk.

" Man ! it was a rale peety ye couldna come to the kirn. Naethin' short o' a broken leg wad hae keepit me awa'. Jings ! auld Baxter did us prood, an' weel he micht, conseederin' hoo we hae wrocht airly and late in the hairst-field gettin' in his crops. But, losh, to see the lot o' us dancin' awa' like linties till fower o'clock i' the mornin', ye wadna ha'e thocht we had juist come to the end o' a lang trauchle i' the fields. Man, it's a queer thing, but when ye're enjoyin' yersel' ye never seem to feel tired.

" The lang granary abune the byre was the scene o' festivities—as ye micht say—an' guidsakes, ye wadna' hae recognised it wi' fancy streamers fleein' aboot the rafters an' Mrs. Baxter's pot-plants flourishin' i' the corners.

" The auld coos doon ablow were unco restive when they heard the stramash up abune, an' noo an' again they wad gi'e a roar fit to wauken the deid, but the competeetion was ower muckle for them. Puir beasts ! They didna' get muckle sleep that nicht, an' I doot the milk pails wad be unco toom next mornin'.

" Wee Sandy cam' alang wi' his fiddle as usual, an' it wasna' lang afore we were stottin' up an' doon the granary like a wheen speugs efter a wurrm. Auld Baxter took the flair first, prancin' like a cairt-horse and hoochin' wi' the best. I followed wi' Mrs. Baxter, an' mind ye, for her size, she was rale licht on her feet, and tho' she did stramp on mine whiles, I had on ma tackety-buits, so it didna maitter muckle.

" We were sune warmed up to the ploy. Nane o' your canny dances for us ! Na ! it was Corn Riggs, Petronella, the Heilan' Fling, an' a' thae rousin' kind.

Fegs, wee Sandy's face was like a hervest-mune in nae time, an' it wasna' lang afore a' the loons had their collars an' jaikets aff.

"Of coorse, we stoppit noo an' again to wat oor thrapples, an' there's nae denyin' we needed it, for the amoont o' stoor we swallowed was byordnar'. Auld Baxter was rale leeberal, baith wi' the food an' the drink. We had muckle meat pies and tairts, an' dads o' Mrs. Baxter's hame-made ginger-breid, forbye conversation lozenges, an' plenty o' the 'Auld Kirk' to wash things doon.

"But, did ye hear aboot Auld Tam, the herd? Jings, yon was a ploy. He was roarin' fou' lang afore midnicht. In fac', he was tryin' to do a dance on his hunkers a' by himsel' i' the middle o' the flair until me an' auld Baxter got haud o' him and persuaded him to gang hame an' sleep it aff. We had a sair job to get him doon the steps an' ootbye, but i' the end we managed it, an' his last words as he staggered awa' were: 'Ach weel, I'm no carin'. It's been a gey dry affair, onywey.'

"Sangs an' recitations? Och ay! Whit's a kirn withoot them? We were rale thankfu' to ha'e a rest noo an' again to tak the wecht aff oor feet.

"Mrs. Baxter took the flair efter a guid deal o' coaxin' (tho' we kent fine she was deein' to perform a' the time), an' rendered 'Comin' thro' the Rye,' as usual. But it ended in a duet, for ane o' the auld coos doon ablow had had mair than she could thole, an' she roared and hoasted till Mrs. Baxter was fair reed i' the face, tryin' to yell her doon. I'm tellin' ye, it was a fair divert, but we daurna lauch for fear auld Baxter wad be offended. So we juist tried to haud it in an' keep oor faces straicht, tho' by the time the sang was feenished, there was nae tellin' whuther it was Mrs. B. or the auld coo wha was comin' thro' the rye.

"In atween sangs we were flingin' conversation lozenges at each ither wi' maist soulfu' messages on them. I got 'I love you' frae Tibby Tamson, but the only ane I had on haund to thraw back at her was 'Not to-night,' whuch was a peety.

"Mebbe ye'll no' believe it, but we had a recitation frae Rab, the orraman chiel'. Ay, ye micht weel cock your lugs. We were a' fair whummled when he took the flair, for he's usually sic a backward loon wi' never a word to say for himsel'. But auld Baxter's generosity maun ha'e been ower muckle for him, for he was in sic an exalted state that he wad ha'e performed afore the King, without turnin' a hair.

"I wadna' ha'e believed he had it in him. Man, he was that opened oot that there was nae stoppin' him ance he was sterted. He went hauf-wey through Rabbie Burns, an' syne begude on Shakespeare nae less, afore wee Sandy got restive, an' sterted up a reel when he was i' the middle o' a lang-wunded verse. He was still recitin' awa' when we were a' hoochin' an' prancin' roond aboot him, an' I daursay he wad still be staundin' there layin't aff if his legs hadna' gied oot on him.

"Auld Baxter himsel' was feelin' the strain by noo, but it affected him in a deeferent wey, for he got mair an' mair polite as the wee sma' hoors cam' on, an' he was usin' lang words that naether him nor onybody else kent the meanin' o'.

"Hooever, afore we scaled (that was when wee Sandy had broken his last fiddle-string, an' was doon to the wud, an' a' the cocks were crawin' i' the yaird), he made an anooncement that we were a' rale gled to hear.

" 'Frien's an' neibours,' quo' he, streikin' up his back, as if he was addressin' the Hooses o' Parliament, ' it gi'es me the maist intensified pleesure, the maist extraordinary happiness to inform ye that I am grantin' ye the favour o' a vacation the morn.' In ither words we had the day aff. So we cheered him till the rafters rattled, an' the auld coos groaned wi' agony, an' syne we a' gaed hame as best we could, an' the kirn was ower for anither year.

" Ay, man ! ma banes were sair the next day, but it was weel worth it."

THE AULD ANGLER.

When Geordie tak's his rod an' line
The fishes seem to ken it fine ;
They jouk awa' ablow the stanes,
An' he gets naethin' for his pains.

Fu' patient aye he'll sit an' cast
Until the day is nearly past ;
Syne stramp awa' wi' little glee
To hae twa kippers to his tea.

THE DYKER.

Wi' horny haunds he tak's the stanes,
Like him, fu' grey an' auld,
An' bigs a beild whaur mony a beast
May shelter frae the cauld.

97

An' ane by ane, wi' muckle care
He sets them i' their place,
An' as the dyke begudes to grow
The pride gleams i' his face.

For weel he kens, though years may gang
An' storms birl ower the brae,
The firm foundation he has laid
Wull stand for mony a day.

THE AULD HERD

Ay, Tweed, ma lad, oor day is dune ;
I'm gettin' no' sae spry.
I'll hae to lay the crook doon sune
An' draw ma chair inbye.

We've dune oor bit baith you an' me,
An' weathered mony a blast ;
We've herded sheep on hill an' lea,
But noo a' that is past.

I'll sit doon at the ingle-nook,
An' ye'll lie by ma side,
An' we'll hae a read in the guid auld Book
That ma mither kept wi' pride.

An' then when nichts are gettin' lang,
An' the blast is bitin' cauld,
The Guid Shepherd'll come alang
An' herd us to His fauld.

When I went back to visit the farm the other day, I was relieved to find Uncle Andra waiting for me at the Station with a gig instead of a car.

" Ay, lassie," said he, helping me in, " this shortage o' petrol's been a real Godsend to me. I've got rid o' yon car at last, an' I'm danged if I'll ever gang back to't. W'hup, Jenny ! " (Uncle Andra's ponies are always called " Jenny," regardless !)

It was a relief to sit beside him on the horsehair-cushioned seat, and know that I could relax for the rest of the journey, as I never could when Uncle Andra was " driving " a car.

He had never adapted himself to the " clutter o' machinery," as he called it. Accustomed to ambling along with a sure-footed horse which knew every step of the way, he could not become reconciled to the fact that he must keep his mind on the " machinery " all the time if he did not want to land in the ditch, which he very frequently did.

He had an alarming habit of taking his hands from the wheel to point out a field of crops and would turn round to gaze at some distant object, while the car did the figure-eight across the road.

Nor did he ever get the hang of the intricacies of the gears, and would forget to change down or up until the car came to a standstill in protest, whereupon Uncle Andra would work himself into a rage and burst out : " Dang it ! What ails ye noo ? Ye're never content for twa meenits thegither. Guidness kens wha invented sic cantraptions as cars ! "

It was a familiar sight on some lonely stretch of road to see the car at a standstill, and Uncle Andra, red with rage, cranking it up with the starting-handle, and muttering invective to relieve his feelings at its unheeding bonnet.

Often it would be found in the end that some simple disorder, such as lack of petrol, had been the cause of the breakdown. Oftener than not, he would be towed home ignominiously, declaring darkly that " that fiendish machinery's let me doon again."

Uncle Andra was so well known on the roads that cautious drivers were wont to turn down side-lanes when they saw him coming. Nor did they pay any attention to his signals, which were so unorthodox that they would have stunned the man who compiled the Highway Code.

But his method of reversing had to be seen to be believed. It was said that he killed a duck or a hen every time he turned the car, and often he became so " fankled " that he walked away from his machine in disgust, and would have abandoned it altogether had not some wellwisher come to the rescue and done the job for him.

The stories about Uncle Andra and his car are legion. There was the day when his horn started to blow and refused to stop, just when he was coming face-to-face with a walking funeral on a narrow country road. There was the day when the car itself wouldn't stop, and he came bounding up the road, and shot past the farm-house, to our astonishment, and sped on for another mile or two until his petrol gave out.

And there was the day he turned a somersault after a skid, and nearly climbed up a telegraph post afterwards. " Dodsakes, the thing's demented ! " he declared, when the car finally shuddered to a standstill half-way up a dry-stane dyke.

Indeed, he has been through so many cantrips with his " machinery " that it is surprising that he (let alone the car which, it must be admitted, is now qualifying for the salvage dump) is alive to tell the tale.

" But nae mair o' that for me," said he, as we jogged placidly along behind Jenny. " Ye can say what ye like aboot yon Hitler, but there's nae doot he's done me a guid turn."

THE PORTER

There's mony men wi' lang degrees
An' fancy education ;
But nane sae prood as Weelum Broon,
The porter at the station.

A sair forfochen chiel is he,
An' aye in sic a steerie ;
Wi' twa trains birlin' by ilk' day
Nae wunner that he's weary.

An' as ilk' train comes rattlin' in,
Auld Weelum blaws a whustle,
An' opens wide the muckle yetts ;
Ma conscience, sic a bustle !

An' : " Auchencrummock," aye he roars
At ilka open cairritch ;
His braith he never thinks to hain
For keepin' cool his pairritch.

A wale o' men is Weelum Broon
In his ain estimation ;
For king o' a' the crood is he
At Auchencrummock station.

THE SINNER

Ilk Sabbath I aye seem sae godly an' douce
As I sit by ma faither, as still as a moose ;
But ma thochts, gin ye kent them, wad gaur the Deil
    smirk,
For they're no' juist the kind ye should think i' the kirk.

When the Beadle gangs up wi' the Book in his haund
I kink to masel', for he looks geyan graund,
An' I *wush* he wad trip doon the auld poopit stairs.
(Sic thochts ! when ma heid should haud naethin' but
    prayers).

Noo the singin' begudes an' we're a' on oor taes,
For it's wha to be loodest in leadin' the praise ;
An' I canna but think, as ma lugs gi'e a stoond,
That shairly the Lord maun be deived wi' the soond.

Mrs. Broon I maun watch as a pandrop she sooks ;
She tries aye to hide it wi' innocent looks,
But I ken fine it's there frae the bulge i' her jaw.
Sic fun it wad be if the poke was to fa' !

An', jings ! when it's time for auld Rab to come roon',
Wi' the plate i' his haund an' a squeak i' his shoon,
He rattles the siller for a' fowk to see,
An' I'm gey sweart to pairt wi' ma Sabbath bawbee.

Ay ! mebbe I aye seem sae godly an' douce
As I sit by my faither, as still as a moose ;
But ma thochts I maun hide, for they're burnin' wi' sin,
(Gin the meenister kent them, he'd ne'er let me in !)

I have just been staying with Aunt Martha in her country cottage. It is a real cottage, not one of those with roses-round-the-door, all modern conveniences, and 'buses passing the end of the road every ten minutes.

It is, more truthfully, a but-and-ben, tucked under the wing of a steep hill. To reach civilisation in the shape of a handful of houses, Aunt Martha has to walk down a narrow pathway for a mile, and follow the bumpy road for another. At the village shop, she can buy paraffin and peppermints (the latter always taste of the former), have her boots repaired, purchase stamps and pills, and hear the latest gossip. For the rest, she relies on a casual van-man, who comes erratically to the foot of the hill, and whistles loudly for her to come down with her shopping-basket.

Yet, in spite of the obvious draw-backs of her isolated life, Aunt Martha's days are as colourful, romantic, and exciting, as those of any film star. And with it all, she remains placid and contented, which cannot be said of the most of us.

It is a delight to watch her cooking. She is as full of surprises as a lucky-bag. One morning, I found that she had been out to the little burn that runs by the foot of the hill and miraculously caught two trout. She cooked them, gipsy-fashion, over the open fire, and we ate them with a brown meal scone of her own baking.

As meal-time approaches, she looks round the kitchen, opens the press door, and says: " What have I got ? One egg, some flour, a little sugar and butter, some jam. Ah ! we'll have Tuesday tarts for tea."

" Why Tuesday tarts, Aunt Martha ? " I ask, amused.

"Why, to-day's Tuesday, of course." And the Tuesday tarts will be delicious, and taste all the better, because of their funny name.

Even in dress, Aunt Martha does not believe in following the crowd. She has a special design of her own which she has found becoming, and she is faithful to it, no matter how often the wheel of fashion turns. She is proud of her trim waist, and has her dresses made with neatly-fitting bodices, and long, flowing skirts, which she often " kilts " up when tramping over the hill in wet weather.

Although she loves people, Aunt Martha is never lonely on her own. She thoroughly enjoys her company, and can sit smiling at her own thoughts for hours on end. But when a wandering packman comes over the hill, she gives him a welcome that warms his heart, and brings him into the shining kitchen, sets him in the rocking-chair, and makes him a cup of strong, black tea, such as only wanderers can appreciate.

It is a real joy to hear Aunt Martha tell of such a visit. When she is telling me about it, she misses no detail of word or look, till I can feel that I have met the old broom-seller or the rag-bag woman and almost hear them speaking.

"Why, Aunt Martha," I say in admiration, " I have hundreds of visitors, and yet I could never describe one of them as you do, or enjoy their visits so much."

"Ah, my dear," she says wisely, " but I take time to enjoy myself. It's a thing that can't be rushed."

When her wealthy friends come to see her—and it is a tribute to Aunt Martha that they come so far and so often—they are rather hurt to think that she can remain so glowingly happy when she is missing all the expensive luxuries of their own lives.

"But what do I miss?" she protests. "Nothing of the real essentials of life. Amusement? You go to theatres or parties for it. I get mine in the garden, coaxing my apple-ringie to grow, or in a hundred other ways. And I do succeed in getting my amusement; I think, perhaps, sometimes you don't."

Yet Aunt Martha has no desire to live a selfishly aloof life, as all the humble people of the village know. Her gift of friendship is not wasted. She is known and loved by all as Aunt Martha, and it is she to whom they turn when in trouble.

"How do you do it, Aunt Martha?" I often ask her, in despair at my own shortcomings. "I get so tired of myself, and yet I live in such a whirl that I'm seldom alone."

"That's just it, my dear," she tells me. "You don't know yourself properly. Believe me, until you take time to be alone, you never get to know what you're like. You're only a casual acquaintance. I have learned to laugh at, and with myself. I have dusted up my faults, and found out one or two good spots that were hidden away in corners. I've begun to appreciate myself and find out the real values of life."

After visiting the cottage, I always go back to town, feeling refreshed and invigorated, and yet a little ashamed of myself. And as I plunge myself into the hundred and one little affairs that make up my day, I wonder if I will ever have the courage to take hold of my life, and remould it into a simpler pattern, as Aunt Martha has done.

FAME

I hae sic yearnin' i' ma hairt
To play some grand an' glorious pairt ;
But I maun mind the hearth an' hame,
An' canna mak' a bid for Fame.
Nae laurel leaves'll croon ma tresses.
(I'm aff to clean the kitchen presses.)

I'd like to think that when I dee
The warld micht whiles remember me,
But, fegs, I never hae the time
To pent a scene or pen a rhyme.
While ithers to the Muse are bendin'
I maun be busy wi' the mendin'.

I dream o' deeds baith brave an' braw,
An' sigh for things I never saw ;
While peelin' tatties at the sink
O' heroines I aften think ;
Yet tho' nae Fame I'll be possessin'
Ma hamely task'll bring a blessin'.

THE GLOAMIN'

Tho' a' ma days an' nichts are black
Wi' ne'er a glint o' licht,
There's mony a lichtsome thing I see
For a' I've lost ma sicht.

An' kindly fowk are wae for me
As i' the mirk I sit,
An' dinna ken that tho' I'm blin',
Ma darkness aye is lit.

For whiles I think o' bonnier things
Than e'en the bricht warld kens ;
An' frien's hae I that flit aroon'
An' licht ma inward lens.

The rain an' sun's alike to me
An' ugliness no' there ;
For i' the gloamin' o' ma life,
Ma visions are a' fair.

THE PRECENTOR

Wi' horny haunds he tak's the fork
An' dings it ower his knee,
Then to his lug he hauds it up,
An' " Do, re, mi," says he.

An' then begudes the solemn praise—
Tho' whiles ower low or high—
But if at first the tune gangs wrang
He gies anither try.

An' as he wrestles wi' the Psalms
An' shouts the ithers doon,
If ony daur to sing ower lood
He gliffs them wi' a froon.

An' when at last the kirk has skailed
An' fowk hae gaen their ways,
They micht forget the text an' prayer
But no' wha leads the praise.

Aiblins, ye've heard tell o' Big Wull, wha's heid bummer in oor village. He tak's pairt in everything, frae ringin' the Kirk bells o' a Sawbath, to killin' soos for the neibourin' fermers. His ain trade's cobblin', but he has his neb in ilka body's business, and there's no' a thing ye could mention but whit Big Wull kens a' aboot it.

He's been unco thrang this while back wi' the War. Mebbe the wheen thoosand sodgers ower at the front doin' a bit o' fechtin' ha'ena heard that it's Big Wull wha's at the heid o' things. But, jings, we ken a' aboot it.

He's got us a' gliffed oot o' oor wuts wi' his talk o' spies hingin' aboot the dyke-sides an' Germans droppin' frae parachutes an' whatnot. We daurna even licht up a pipe when we're oot i' the village street efter derk. He's that parteekler aboot the black-oot that ye'd think we were richt fornent the front line itsel'.

A'weel, a'e nicht when he was paradin' aboot, as prood as a cock on a midden, an' glowerin' roond for ony flaw i' the black-oot, a muckle flare lichted up the hale village.

"Goveydick," roared Big Wull, grippin' his tin helmet. "The Germans are here."

Wi' that he blew a blast on his whustle that wad ha'e waukened the deid, an' syne a' the fowk (except a wheen wha had creepit ablow their beds for shelter) cam' skelterin' to the doors to see whit the steerie was aboot.

Big Wull stuck oot his chest, an' went stottin' doon the street, as if he was gaun to do big things.

"I'll tackle them," cries he to the beadle, who was daun'erin' aboot like a knotless threid. "Hoo mony bombs ha'e they drappit?"

"Nane ava'," quo' the beadle, "It's somebody's lum on fire."

Big Wull's coontenance fell. It was a sair disappointment efter he had been expec'in' to win the V.C., at least, for his gallant conduct.

"A lum on fire !" he roared, fair dancin' wi' rage. "Spilin' ma guid black-oot. Wha's the culprit ? Wait till I lay ma haunds on him. Sic carelessness as this maun be reported to the Government."

He went breezin' doon the street as if the de'il was efter him, but when he cam' nearer the conflagration, his steps kind o' faltered, for it was his ain chimney that was bleezin' awa'.

Ay, puir Wull ! He didna sing sae croose efter that. He hummed and hawed for a whilie, an' syne sent the Beadle aff for the Fire Brigade—in ither words, the hauflin loon wi' twa buckets o' watter, an' a wee bit hose-pipe that's naither here nor there.

They put oot the fire a' richt, but some o' Big Wull's pride went wi't. He's still rinnin' the War, of coorse, but he thinks twice noo afore he mak's a sang when he sees a chink o' licht showin'.

HERO

I'd like to be a hero brave
An' send a dragon to its grave,
Or clout a giant ower the heid—
I rin the messages instead !

I'll never hae a noble name,
Ma mither needs me aye at hame
To cairt the coal an' scour the stair—
An', och ! ma back is aften sair.

An' whiles when scrubbin' oot the sink
Heroic thochts I aften think ;
An' aye I wush't wi' a' ma hairt
That I could play a princely pairt ;

But, hoots, it seems that folk like me
Maun bide at hame an' mask the tea,
An' leave the noble deeds to men
Wha're no' sae thrang—an' mair than ten !

ON LEAVE

Oor Tam's come hame a canny chiel,
I doot he canna feel sae weel,
He's geyan wearie.
I ken he's been to see the King,
But still he doesna say a thing
Aboot the steerie.

He'll sit aroond an' mend the clock
Or do some ither triflin' trock,
An' aye he'll speir ;
" Hoo mony kittlin's had the cat ? "
An' silly, hamely things like that.
It's unco queer !

I want to hear o' noble deeds,
But Tam, he lauchs an' never heeds,
Syne oot he wuns
To potter wi' the gairden gate :
He's mair consairned aboot *its* fate
Than wi' the Huns.

He'd raither hear aboot the hens,
But what he's seen or what he kens
He winna say ;
Tho' whiles, when ower the dambrod peerin',
I ken his thochts are unco steerin'
An' far away.

THE MEENISTER

Wi' earnest neives he thumps the Buik
To mak' his text mair clear,
An' roars sae lood that a' the kirk
His prophecies micht hear.

His airms he flings baith east an' wast,
His haun's flee a' the airts,
As on he rants o' Heeven an' Hell
(Divided i' three pairts).

An' mony a pandrop's sookit dry
Afore the sermon's ower,
An' mony a snooze is hidden frae
The preacher's wrathfu' glower.

But tho' his sermons may be driech
An' fearsome be his roar,
The meenister's a welcome sicht
At ilka cottage door.

For aye when trouble dims the hoose
An' waefu' hairts are sair,
The meenister's the first to come
An' gie his help an' prayer.

THE AULD DOMINIE

The schule is dowie noo they've gane
An' left me sittin' here alane,
Wi' ghaistly faces a' aroon',
An' nane to fear ma lichtest froon.

The eident tawse lies on the flair ;
They'll feel its dirlin' stang nae mair,
For noo ma skelpin' days are past
An' I maun leave ma desk at last.

Aroon' the sates I cast ma een,
Whaur mony a quakin' scholar's been ;
An' there, at Poochie Tamson's place
I seem to see his lichtsome face.

Nae lad o' pairts that chiel'll be !
An', fegs ! the ploys he's played on me !
But tho' he plunked an' palmies got
I lo'ed him best o' a' the lot.

The de'il ! He's drawn me on his slate !
I'll crack the loonie ower the pate . .
But, na, anither maister noo
Maun rant an' rule the weans I lo'e.

A' weel, I'll steek the door an' gang.
Ma memories'll keep ma thrang ;
An' whiles, nae doot, the bairns'll mind,
In spite o' skelps, ma hairt was kind.